Nuffield Primary Science
SCIENCE PROCESSES AND CONCEPT EXPLORATION

"Bellyeoman" Primary School

Forces and movement

Ages
7-12

TEACHERS' GUIDE

PUBLISHED FOR THE NUFFIELD–CHELSEA CURRICULUM TRUST BY COLLINS EDUCATIONAL

NUFFIELD PRIMARY SCIENCE
Science Processes and Concept Exploration

Directors
Paul Black
Wynne Harlen

Deputy Director
Terry Russell

Project members
Robert Austin
Derek Bell
Adrian Hughes
Ken Longden
John Meadows
Linda McGuigan
Jonathan Osborne
Pamela Wadsworth
Dorothy Watt

First published 1993 by Collins Educational
An imprint of HarperCollins*Publishers*
77-85 Fulham Palace Road
London W6 8JB

Second edition published 1995
Reprinted 1996, 1997

Copyright © Nuffield-Chelsea Curriculum Trust 1993, 1995

ISBN 0 00 310255 6

Printed and bound by Scotprint Ltd, Musselburgh

Design by Carla Turchini, Chi Leung
Illustrations by Gay Galsworthy, Maureen Hallahan,
Mary Lonsdale, Sally Neave, Karen Tushingham,
Jakki Wood
Cover artwork by Karen Tushingham

Photograph acknowledgements
Page 28: Science Photo Library
Page 29: Allsport
Page: 41: NES Arnold
Page 50: Zefa
Page 62: John Birdsall
Page 65: John Birdsall
Page 76: Brian Shuel
Page 79: John Birdsall

Commissioned photography by Oliver Hatch

The Trust and the Publishers would like to thank the
governors, staff and pupils of Hillbrook Primary School,
Tooting, for their kind co-operation with many of the
photographs in this book.

Safety adviser
Peter Borrows

Other contributors
Elizabeth Harris
Carol Joyes
Anne de Normanville
Ralph Hancock

Trial schools

The SPACE Project and the Trust are grateful to the
governors, staff, and pupils of all the trial schools. It will
be obvious to readers of these guides how much we are
indebted to them for their help, and especially for the
children's drawn and written records of their hard work
and their growing understanding of science.

All Saints Primary School, Barnet, Hertfordshire
Ansdell County Primary School, Lytham St Anne's,
Lancashire
Bishop Endowed Church of England Junior School,
Blackpool
Brindle Gregson Lane Primary School, Lancashire
Brookside Junior and Infants School, Knowsley
Chalgrove JMI School, Finchley, London N3
Christ the King Roman Catholic Primary School, Blackpool
English Martyrs Roman Catholic Primary School,
Knowsley
Fairlie County Primary School, Skelmersdale, Lancashire
Fairway JMI School, Mill Hill, London NW7
Foulds Primary School, Barnet, Hertfordshire
Frenchwood County Primary School, Preston
Grange Park Primary School, London N21
Hallesville Primary School, Newham, London E6
Heathmore Primary School, Roehampton, London SW15
Honeywell Junior School, London SW11
Huyton Church of England Junior School, Knowsley
Longton Junior School, Preston
Mawdesley Church of England Primary School, Lancashire
Moor Park Infants School, Blackpool
Mosscroft County Primary School, Knowsley
Nightingale Primary School, London E18
Oakhill Primary School, Woodford Green, Essex
Park Brow County Primary School, Knowsley
Park View Junior School, Knowsley
Purford Green Junior School, Harlow, Essex
Ronald Ross Primary School, London SW19
Rosh Pinah School, Edgeware, Middlesex
Sacred Heart Junior School, Battersea, London SW11
St Aloysius Roman Catholic Infants School, Knowlsey
St Andrew's Roman Catholic Primary School, Knowsley
St Bernadette's Roman Catholic Primary School, Blackpool
St James's Church of England Junior School, Forest Gate,
London E7
St John Fisher Roman Catholic Primary School, Knowsley
St John Vianney Roman Catholic Primary School,
Blackpool
St Mary and St Benedict Roman Catholic Primary School,
Bamber Bridge, Preston
St Peter and St Paul Roman Catholic Primary School,
Knowsley
St Theresa's Roman Catholic Primary School, Blackpool
St Theresa's Roman Catholic Primary School, Finchley,
London N3
Scarisbrick County Primary School, Lancashire
Selwyn Junior School, London E4
Snaresbrook Primary School, Wanstead, London E18
South Grove Primary School, Walthamstow, London E17
Southmead Infants School, London SW19
Staining Church of England Primary School, Blackpool
Walton-le-Dale County Primary School, Preston
West Vale County Primary School, Kirkby
Woodridge Primary School, North Finchley, London N12

Contents

Explanation of symbols in the margins

 Warning

 Good opportunities to develop and assess work related to Experimental and Investigative Science.

 Notes which may be useful to the teacher

 Vocabulary work

 Opportunities for children to use information technology

 Equipment needed

 Reference to the pupils' books

CHAPTER 1

Introduction

1.1 The SPACE approach to teaching and learning science

A primary class where the SPACE approach to science is being used may not at first seem different from any other class engaged in science activities; in either, children will be mentally and physically involved in exploring objects and events in the world around them. However, a closer look will reveal that both the children's activities and the teacher's role differ from those found in other approaches. The children are not following instructions given by others; they are not solving a problem set them by someone else. They are deeply involved in work which is based on their own ideas, and they have taken part in deciding how to do it.

The teacher has, of course, prepared carefully to reach the point where children try out their ideas. She or he will have started on the topic by giving children opportunities to explore from their own experience situations which embody important scientific ideas. The teacher will have ensured that the children have expressed their ideas about what they are exploring, using one or more of a range of approaches – from whole class discussion to talking with individual children, or asking children to write or draw – and will have explored the children's reasons for having those ideas.

With this information the teacher will have decided how to help the children to develop or revise their ideas. That may involve getting the children to use the ideas to make a prediction, then testing it by seeing if it works in practice; or the children may gather further evidence to discuss and think about. In particular, the teacher will note how 'scientific' children have been in their gathering and use of evidence; and should, by careful questioning, encourage greater rigour in the use of scientific process skills.

It is essential that the children change their ideas only as a result of what they find themselves, not by merely accepting ideas which they are told are better.

By carefully exploring children's ideas, taking them seriously and choosing appropriate ways of helping the children to test them, the teacher can move children towards ideas which apply more widely and fit the evidence better – those which are, in short, more scientific.

You will find more information about the SPACE approach in the Nuffield Primary Science *Science Co-ordinators' handbook*.

1.2 Useful strategies

Finding out children's ideas

This guide points out many opportunities for finding out children's ideas. One way is simply by talking, but there are many others. We have found the following strategies effective. How you use them may depend on the area of science you are dealing with. In Chapter 3 you will find examples of these strategies. More information about them is given in the *Science Co-ordinators' handbook*.

Talking and open questioning

Whole class discussions can be useful for sharing ideas, but they do not always give all children a chance to speak. It is often helpful if children are allowed to think of their own ideas first, perhaps working them out in drawings, and are then encouraged to share these with others – perhaps with just one other child, or with a larger group.

Annotated drawings

Asking children to draw their ideas can give a particularly clear insight into what they think. It also gives you a chance to discuss the children's ideas with them. Words conveying these ideas can then be added to the drawing, either by you or by the child. Such work can be kept as a permanent record.

Sorting and classifying

This can be a useful way of helping children to clarify their ideas and to record their thinking. They could sort a collection of objects or pictures into groups.

Writing down ideas

Children may instead write down their responses to questions you pose. Writing gives children the opportunity to express their own views, which can then be shared with others or investigated further.

Log books and diaries

These can be used to record changes over a longer investigation. They need not necessarily be kept by individual children, but could be kept by a whole group or class. Children can jot down their ideas, as words or drawings, when they notice changes, recording their reasons for what they observe.

Helping children to develop their ideas

Letting children test their own ideas

This will involve children in using some or all of the process skills of science:

- observing
- measuring
- hypothesizing
- predicting
- planning and carrying out fair tests
- interpreting results and findings
- communicating

It is an important strategy which can, and should, be used often. The *use* of process skills *develops* them – for example, through greater attention to detail in observing, more careful control of variables in fair tests, and taking all the evidence into account in interpreting the results.

Encouraging generalization from one context to another

Does an explanation proposed for a particular event fit one which is not exactly the same, but which involves the same scientific concept? You or the children might suggest other contexts that might be tried. This might be done by discussing the evidence for and against the explanation, or by gathering more evidence and testing the idea in the other context, depending on children's familiarity with the events being examined.

Discussing the words children use to describe their ideas

Children can be asked to be quite specific about the meaning of words they use, whether scientific or not. They can be prompted to think of alternative words which have almost the same meaning. They can discuss, where appropriate, words which have special meaning in a scientific context, and so be helped to realize the difference between the 'everyday' use of some words and the scientific one.

Extending the range of evidence

Some of the children's ideas may be consistent with the evidence at present available to them, but could be challenged by extending the range of evidence. This applies particularly to things which are not easily observed, such as slow changes; or those which are normally hidden, such as the insides of objects. Attempts to make these imperceptible things perceptible, often by using secondary sources, help children to consider a wider range of evidence.

Getting children to communicate their ideas

Expressing ideas in any way – through writing, drawing, modelling or, particularly, through discussion – involves thinking them through, and often rethinking and revising them. Discussion has a further advantage in that it is two-way and children can set others' ideas against their own. Just realizing that there are different ideas helps them to reconsider their own.

1.3 Equal opportunities

The SPACE approach to teaching and learning science gives opportunities for every child to build on and develop his or her experiences, skills and ideas. It can therefore be used to benefit pupils of all kinds and at any stage of development. This is fully discussed in the *Science Co-ordinators' handbook*.

1.4 Forces and movement and the curriculum

This teachers' guide is divided into four themes; in each one there is a section on finding out children's ideas, examples of ideas children have, and a section on helping children to develop their ideas.

Nuffield Primary Science Themes

Moving things

This theme explores the ways in which a wide variety of things move on land, water and in the air. The factors which affect the movement of objects are also investigated. All children can give examples of things that move and many recognize that some things can be moved by pushing or pulling them. When there is no obvious push or pull the reasons suggested for the movement vary considerably and are often specific to the object or vehicle. Some children indicate that gravity causes things to fall but very few give it as a cause for something moving down a slope. The activities explore the wide range of things that move and provide examples of practical investigations that look at the factors influencing the movement of an object.

Stopping and staying put

This theme is very closely linked to that of 'Moving things', but it concentrates very specifically on exploring why things stop moving or are not moving. The idea and importance of friction is introduced. Many children recognize that there is something that stops things moving, but offer many different reasons which are usually specific to a given situation. Words such as grip and stick are used by children, suggesting that they have some idea of friction which can be developed. The activities suggested provide opportunities for children to investigate why things stop or are not moving. These look at ways of stopping ourselves moving and testing different ways of stopping moving objects.

Floating and sinking

This theme provides opportunities for children to investigate the factors involved in floating and sinking. Children often suggest that heavy things sink and light things float. The depth of water under the object is something given as a reason why some things sink and others float. Few children suggest that there is a combination of factors involved and/or that the water is pushing up to keep the object afloat. The activities suggested test a number of factors that might affect what floats and what doesn't. Ways of experiencing the upthrust of the water and measuring it are described.

Structures and balance

This theme explores how forces influence the stability of structures and the way in which forces work with and against each other in a variety of situations. Children will often build a structure or make something balance intuitively but will suggest reasons that only describe the structure. They rarely refer to ideas of stability, the effects of gravity or that something is pushing/pulling against something else in the structure. The activities provide opportunities for investigating a range of structures through visits to examine buildings, bridges etc. and through practical tests in school. Much of the work is designed to provide experiences from which work at Key Stage 3 can be developed.

National Curriculum Programmes of Study	Environmental Studies 5-14 (Scotland): Science
Physical Processes **2 Forces and motion** **b** that objects have weight because of the gravitational attraction between them and the Earth; **c** about friction, including air resistance, as a force which slows moving objects; **d** that when springs and elastic bands are stretched they exert a force on whatever is stretching them; **f** that forces act in particular directions; **g** that forces acting on an object can balance and that when this happens an object at rest stays still; **h** that unbalanced forces can make things speed up, slow down, or change direction.	**Understanding Energy and Forces (Stages P4 to P6)** **Forces and their effects** • motion down a slope under gravity; • air resistance, streamlining.
Physical Processes **2 Forces and motion** **c** about friction, including air resistance, as a force which slows moving objects; **f** that forces act in particular directions; **g** that forces acting on an object can balance and that when this happens an object at rest stays still; **h** that unbalanced forces can make things speed up, slow down, or change direction.	**Understanding Energy and Forces (Stages P4 to P6)** **Forces and their effects** • friction forces on different surfaces, reducing friction; • force of gravity.
Physical Processes **2 Forces and motion** **f** that forces act in particular directions; **g** that forces acting on an object can balance and that when this happens an object at rest stays still; **h** that unbalanced forces can make things speed up, slow down, or change direction.	**Understanding Energy and Forces (Stages P4 to P6)** **Forces and their effects** • friction forces on different surfaces, reducing friction.
Physical Processes **2 Forces and motion** **b** that objects have weight because of the gravitational attraction between them and the Earth; **f** that forces act in particular directions; **g** that forces acting on an object can balance, and that when this happens an object at rest stays still; **h** that unbalanced forces can make things speed up, slow down, or change direction.	**Understanding Energy and Forces** **Forces and their effects** Leading on to (Stages P7 to S2) • the lever as a force magnifier; • simple pulley systems; • simple gear systems; • measurements of forces, spring balance.

1.5 Experimental and Investigative Science

Two important aspects of children's learning in science are:

◆ learning how to investigate the world around them;
◆ learning to make sense of the world around them using scientific ideas.

These are reflected in the National Curriculum. 'Experimental and Investigative Science' covers the first aspect. The second aspect is covered by the rest of the Programme of Study. Although these two aspects of science learning are separated in the National Curriculum they cannot be separated in practice and it is not useful to try to do so. Through investigation children explore their ideas and/or test out the ideas which arise from discussion. As a result, ideas may be advanced, but this will depend on the children's investigation skills. Thus it is important to develop these skills in the context of activities which extend ideas. So there is no separate Nuffield Primary Science teachers' guide on scientific investigations, because opportunities to make these occur throughout all the guides and they form an essential part of the SPACE approach.

Thus in this guide you will find investigations which provide opportunities to develop and assess the skills and understanding set out in Experimental and Investigative Science. These are marked in the text by the symbol shown here. In this teachers' guide, the investigations which cover the most skills are 'Extending the starter activity [floating and sinking in the classroom]' (page 69) and 'Building structures' (page 89).

It is important that teachers give active guidance to pupils during investigations to help them work out how to improve the way in which they plan and carry out their investigations.

Experimental and Investigative Science is about the ways scientific evidence can be obtained, about the ways observations and measurements are made, and about the way in which the evidence is analysed. It therefore sets out three main ways in which pupils can develop their ability to do experimental and investigative science, as follows:-

1 'Planning experimental work'. Here, children should be helped to make progress from asking general and vague questions, to suggesting ideas which could be tested. Teachers' discussion with pupils should aim to help them to make predictions, using their existing understanding, on the basis of which they can decide what evidence should be collected. This should lead them to think about what apparatus and equipment they should use.

When children describe plans for their work, they should be helped to think about what features they are going to change, what effects of these changes they are going to observe or measure, and what features they must keep the same. In this way they can come to understand what is meant by 'a fair test'.

2 'Obtaining evidence'. Children should make observations in the light of their ideas about what they are looking for and why. When they describe their observations, teachers may have to help them to improve, for example by reminding them of their original aims and plan for the work. Such help should also encourage progress from qualitative comparisons and judgements to appreciating the value of making quantitative measurements (for example 'cold water' is qualitative, 'water at 12°C' is quantitative). This should lead to the development of skills with a variety of instruments and to increasing care and accuracy in measurement, involving, for example, repeating measurements to check.

3 'Considering evidence'. Here, children should first learn to record their evidence in systematic and clear ways, starting with simple drawings and then learning to use tables, bar charts and line graphs to display the patterns in numerical data. Then they should be asked to think about and discuss their results, considering what might be learnt from any trends or patterns. As ideas develop, they should be careful in checking their evidence against the original idea underlying the investigation and should become increasingly critical in discussing alternative explanations which might fit their evidence. In such discussions, they should be helped to relate their arguments to their developing scientific understanding. They should also be guided to see possibilities for conducting their investigation more carefully, or in quite different ways.

Whilst these three may seem to form a natural sequence of stages, children's work might not follow this particular sequence. For example, some might start with evidence from their observations and proceed on this basis to propose a hypothesis and a plan to test it. For others, the results of one task may be the starting point for a new inquiry involving new measurements. Useful learning about how to investigate might arise when only one or two of the above aspects of an investigation are involved, or when the teacher tells children about some aspects so that they can concentrate on others. However, there should be some occasions for all pupils when they carry out the whole process of investigation by themselves.

The assessment examples given in chapter 4 are analysed in relation to the level descriptions, which describe children's progress in relation to these three aspects: *planning experimental work, obtaining evidence* and *considering evidence*. Thus, these three provide a framework both for guiding children and for assessing their progress in experimental and investigative work.

CHAPTER 2

Planning

2.1 Introduction: planning with children's ideas in mind

The key scientific ideas presented in this guide can be explored in various contexts, and many of the suggested activities can be incorporated into cross-curricular topic work. This chapter uses a worked example as an aid to planning a topic. Further information on planning is given in the *Science Co-ordinators' handbook.*

A teacher using the SPACE approach should take into account:

◆ the need to find out children's own ideas, not only at the beginning of the work but also at intervals during it;
◆ the importance of planning the investigations with the children, using their ideas as the starting point;
◆ the concepts that are being explored;
◆ the direction in which the children's ideas are developing.

2.2 Cross-curricular topics

Activities which explore the ideas covered in this teachers' guide to *Forces and movement* may be approached via a number of topics in addition to the one set out as an example in the planning sheets (pages 15–16). It is assumed that teachers will adapt the topic to whatever local resources are of interest and readily to hand. Some possibilities are given below.

The fairground

The different forms of motion provided by swings, slides, roundabouts, see-saws and more hair-raising rides can be observed and described. Children might consider the design features, perhaps making models and exploring what makes a piece of apparatus work well: how do you get more slide into a slide, more swing into a swing, a smooth spin on a roundabout, a balance on a see-saw? Starting and stopping are important considerations in terms of the forces involved.
The sounds and sensations of the fairground could provide a stimulus for language work.
There should also be scope for measurement of time (how long the roundabout spins, perhaps with different loads), distance (slide), angles (swing), mass (bodies on see-saws) and so on.

Some links with other Nuffield Primary Science teachers' guides and pupils' books include:

Light – light and colours of the fairground;
Sound and music – fairground sounds;
Using energy – examples of using energy in different ways.

Transport

This topic might begin with children describing the means of getting around which they have used themselves: prams and push chairs, roller skates and scooters, tricycles, bicycles and pedal cars; ice skates, skis and toboggans might be appropriate starting points in the winter months.

Children could consider how these various machines enable movement to take place and how that movement is improved or restricted.

Self-powered vehicles might be a development: motor cycles, cars, trains (what advantages do rails provide?) and trams, aeroplanes, helicopters, hot air balloons, sailing ships, paddle steamers, and submarines (floating and sinking?).

Materials used in making a car or bicycle: how have these changed since they were first invented?

Effects of changing the way a material is used, such as from a solid tyre to an air-filled one: advantages and disadvantages of each.

Properties of metals needed for safe car body construction.

Metal ships, wooden ships and fibre glass boats: advantages of each kind of material.

Construction of ships and boats: joints and moulds.

Airships and balloons: kind of material needed for each.

Materials suitable for aircraft and spaceships.

Transport in different places.

Many children own bicycles, so a sense of ownership of the topic can be fostered; if the school is one in which children are permitted to ride bicycles to school, the resource will be easily available.

The historical development of bicycles might be researched, especially if museum specimens are within reach.

The use of stabilizers or three-wheels could provide an introduction to balance.

The moving parts might be observed and described: axles, pedals, gear wheels, steering, brakes.

Stopping, starting and gripping (tyre and brake blocks) can all be approached through this topic – a good opportunity to talk about road safety .

Some links with other Nuffield Primary Science teachers' guides and pupils' books include:

Materials – materials for making bicycles.

Getting around

Animal movement, particularly human movement, can be a rich source of material for thinking about forces.

The physiology of movement, the way muscles contract and joints permit limbs to articulate, is very relevant.

The variety of ways in which different species such as kangaroos, fish, birds, horses, snails, and worms move might be an interesting way of linking the mechanics of movement to species variation.

Compare the effectiveness of movement in terms of speed and distances travelled.

Bird migration: routes and patterns.

Some links with other Nuffield Primary Science teachers' guides and pupils' books include:

The variety of life – range of animals and methods of moving around, plant movement;
Living processes – how things move, muscles and bones, effects of movement on the body, exercise and health.

Sports and games

Variety of sports and games.
Rules.
Clothing and equipment used.
Need for pushes, pulls, hits, twists and turns.
History of different games.
Games played in different parts of the world.
Organizing a sports event.
Measuring of distance, time and speed records.
The Olympics and other great sporting occasions.

Some links with other Nuffield Primary Science teachers' guides and pupils' books include:

Materials – types of material used for clothing and equipment.

Road safety

Types of vehicles.
Traffic surveys around home and school.
Danger areas and accident black spots.
Causes of accidents.
Speed and braking distances.
Ways of preventing accidents and reducing injuries.
Design of vehicles and road systems.
Warning signs and signals; the Highway code/green cross code.
Safe colours and visibility; mirrors, lights (street and vehicle).

Some links with other Nuffield Primary Science teachers' guides and pupils' books include:

Light – mirrors, signals, colours;
Using energy – fuel sources, effects of speed on fuel consumption;
Materials – materials used for vehicles; clothing, including helmets and brakes.

2.3 Topic plan examples

The following plans illustrate how the science related to *Forces and movement* may be embedded in a cross-curricular topic. The topic presented is 'Transport' and opportunities for exploring mathematics, language, history, geography, design technology and art have been indicated on the first plan. On the second plan the science work has been amplified to illustrate possible areas of exploration based within the overall topic. It is important to remember that these are only examples and are not intended to be exhaustive.

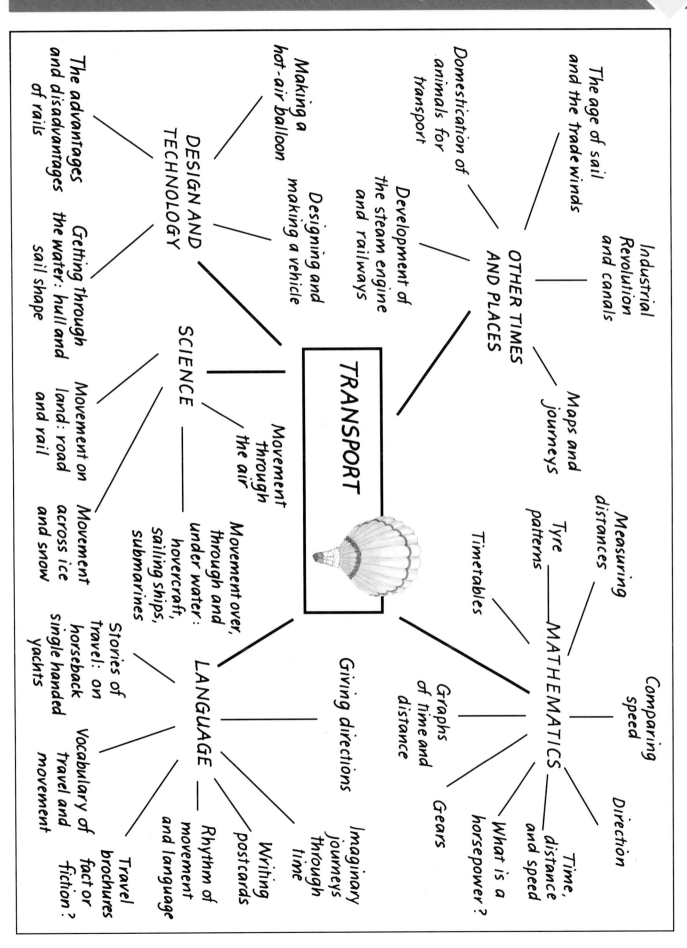

TRANSPORT

OTHER TIMES AND PLACES

The age of sail and the trade winds

Domestication of animals for transport

Development of the steam engine and railways

Industrial Revolution and canals

Maps and journeys

MATHEMATICS

Measuring distances

Tyre patterns

Timetables

Comparing speed

Time, distance and speed

Direction

What is a horsepower?

Gears

Graphs of time and distance

Imaginary journeys through time

DESIGN AND TECHNOLOGY

Making a hot-air balloon

Designing and making a vehicle

The advantages and disadvantages of rails

SCIENCE

Getting through the water: hull and sail shape

Movement on land: road and rail

Movement across ice and snow

Movement through the air

Movement over, through and under water: hovercraft, sailing ships, submarines

LANGUAGE

Stories of travel: on horseback single handed yachts

Giving directions

Writing postcards

Rhythm of movement and language

Vocabulary of travel and movement

Travel brochures fact or fiction?

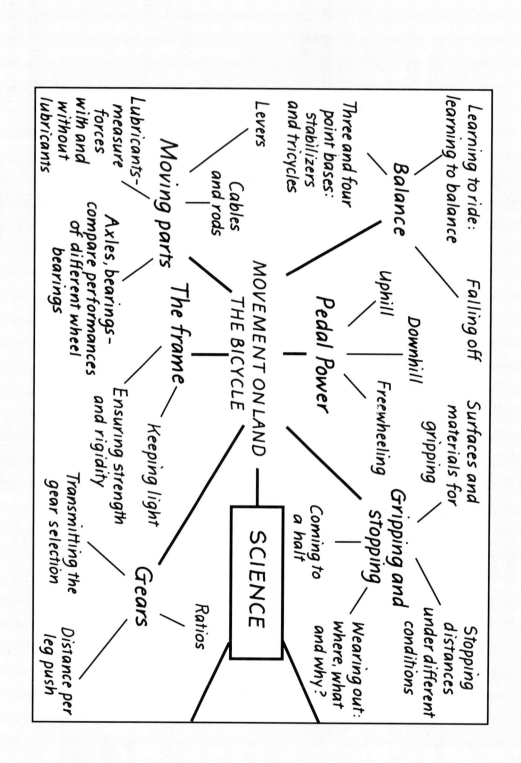

2.4 Use of information technology

 Specific examples of opportunities to use information technology are indicated by this symbol in the margin and referred to in the text. The examples include:

◆ word processing to produce reports of investigations;
◆ the use of software to deal with results and produce charts;
◆ use of computer-based simulation materials.

2.5 Pupils' books

The pupils' books accompanying this guide are called *Forces and Movement* for the lower juniors and *More About Forces and Movement* for the upper juniors. The pupil books are intended to be used spread by spread. The spreads are not sequential, and they are covered in these notes in thematic order.

Features of the pupils' books include:
◆ Stimulus spreads, often visual, designed to raise questions, arouse curiosity, and to promote discussion.

◆ Information spreads, which give secondary source material in a clear and attractive way.

◆ Activity ideas, to form the basis of investigations to be carried out by the children.

◆ Cross-curricular spreads and stories which can act as a basis for creative writing, or spreads with a historical or creative focus.

◆ Real life examples of applications of science in the everyday world.

Forces and movement

Making pancakes pages 2–3

Purpose: A starting point for a discussion of the forces found in everyday life.
Teachers' guide cross-reference: Forces and movement, page 46.

Huff puff and blow pages 16–17

Purpose: A discussion spread to introduce wind or air power, and to show examples.
Note: What is missing from the pictures is the most popular use of wind power – the washing line.
Extension activities: Collect some of the items shown in the pictures on page 16, and display them in the classroom. Children could make their own model windmill. They could list the possible disadvantages of large-scale use of wind power (the windmills are ugly, take up a lot of space, etc.).
Pupils' book cross-references: More about rocks, soil and weather, pages 18-19.

Teachers' guide cross-references: Forces and movement, page 92.

Walking up the wall pages 18–19

Purpose: To show how animals and people hang on against the force of gravity, using grippers and centrifuge – a 'wow' spread children can use on their own.
Notes: The runners keep the roller-coaster cars on track, and both people and cars also depend on centrifugal force. The people also have seat belts to stop them falling out.
Teachers' guide cross-references: Forces and movement, pages 48-9.

Forces in action pages 20–21

Purpose: To provide a fun activity spread and, again, to get away from the idea that forces are always linked to transport.
Extension activities: Try hopscotch and marbles games from spread.
Teachers' guide cross-references: Forces and movement, pages 14, 38, 102.

A push-pull start pages 22–23

Purpose: To help children think about forces in everyday life.
Note: The idea is for children to write captions to go with the story board, using the vocabulary of forces.
Teachers' guide cross-references: Forces and movement, pages 46, 102.

Wheels and tyres pages 6–7

Purpose: To help children develop their ideas about gripping and slipping.
Extension activities: Discuss why we need treads – especially in the winter (prevent slipping, to funnel water out and to stop the car from aqua-planing). Some fashion shoes copy the principle of using a tread.
Teachers' guide cross-references: Forces and movement, pages 14, 15, 60, 103-4.

Gripping and sliding pages 8–9

Purpose: A continuation of pages 6–7, with a sorting activity.
Extension activities: Suggest to the children that they look at their own shoes and see what sort of treads they have on their soles. They could make patterns of imprints, using old shoes. Children could try using a force (or newton) meter in their work in this context (see page 41). They could test their own shoes by dragging them along different surfaces such as a shiny floor, a carpet, and so on.
Teachers' guide cross-references: Forces and movement, pages 56, 102-4.

Moving on water pages 4–5

Purpose: To extend children's understanding of floating and sinking.
Notes: The ships are: a Roman galley, powered by slaves; an 18th century galleon, powered by the wind; a 19th century paddle-steamer with a coal-powered engine; a submarine, which may use nuclear power or diesel fuel; a dinghy, powered by wind; a hovercraft, which travels on a cushion of air and is powered by diesel fuel; a canoe, powered by people using paddles.
Extension activity: Discuss how boats sink.

Teachers' guide cross-references: Forces and movement, pages 13, 15, 44-6, 73-4, 103, 110.

Water power pages 14–15

Purpose: To look at the force of water and how it is used, and to point out its dangers.
Extension activity: The class could make a paddle boat, or a water wheel.
Teachers' guide cross-references: Forces and movement, pages 45-6.

Balancing act pages 10–11

Purpose: To look at forces in balance.
Extension activities: The class could think about this further in PE lessons, and discuss how they achieve balance in different ways. They could make simple balancing toys like the parrot, whose head weighs the same as its tail, and link this to work in technology.
Teachers' guide cross-references: Forces and movement, pages 78-9, 91-3, 109.

Carrying things pages 12–13

Purpose: To provide more examples of balanced forces.
Note: It is easier to carry a baby than a suitcase because it is held closer to the body so the force goes more nearly down the centre of the body.
Extension activities: Children could do a design and technology activity: they could think about the different ways to carry a lunch box or a bag, and look at the different handles on their bags and lunch boxes. Are they successful or not? Why? Encourage them to look at the objects on page 13, and design something to carry each one.
Teachers' guide cross-reference: Forces and movement, pages 15, 102.

More about forces and movement

On the move pages 2–3

Purpose: To provide opportunities for open-ended discussion.
Teachers' guide cross-references: Forces and movement, pages 30, 46.

Life force pages 4–5

Purpose: A 'wow' spread which looks at remarkable examples of forces in nature.
Note: The dinosaur *Pachycephalosaurus* had a skull 60cm long, with bone 25cm thick at the top.
Pupils' book cross-references: More about living things in action, pages 18-19, 22-23.
Teachers' guide cross-reference: Forces and movement, page 46.

A change of direction pages 6–7

Purpose: To provide an introduction to pulleys, cogs and gears.
Note: Explain that cogs, gears etc. can speed up and slow down movement, and change the direction of a force.
Extension activities: Children could build their own pulleys, gears etc. using Legotechnic or other construction kits. Bring in examples of the items listed in the box on page 7. Get children to work in groups,

looking at one of the things listed and taking it in turns to describe their chosen item. Make a link with work in technology. Children can make their own models which use gears.
Teachers' guide cross-references: Forces and movement, pages 46, 50; *Using energy,* pages 81, 84–5.

Lifting and shifting things pages 8–9

Purpose: To introduce the ideas about forces through the medium of a story.
Note: Discuss safety aspects of the story.
Extension activity: The children could use a newton meter to test the weights they can lift with a pulley (care!).

Jet propulsion pages 10–11

Purpose: To introduce the idea of equal and opposite forces.
Extension activities: Ask children how a jet aircraft travels forward. (It pushes air out, backwards). Get the class to predict what will happen to a balloon if it is blown up and let go. In which direction will it fly?
Teachers' guide cross-references: Forces and movement, pages 13, 31, 46; *Using energy,* page 74.

Hovercraft pages 14–15

Purpose: To provide a 'how it works' spread in a real life context.
Note: The photograph on page 15 shows a hovercraft in use in the Everglades in Florida, where it is used because the water is shallow. It is dangerous to the manatees that live there.
Extension activity: Children can make their own hovercraft, using a cardboard tube over a polystyrene tray. If they blow into the tube, they can create an air cushion.
Teachers' guide cross-references: Forces and movement, pages 13, 15.

Twisting and turning pages 16–17

Purpose: To provide a 'fun' reading activity.
Teachers' guide cross-reference: Forces and movement, page 46.

Look, no engine! pages 20–21

Purpose: To help children consider things moving in different ways.
Notes: The balloon floats because it is filled with hot air, which is lighter than the cold air around it. The skier travels downhill fast because there is little friction to hold her back as gravity pulls her downwards. She will go back up in a lift, or she could walk. The helium gas in the balloon is lighter than the gases in the surrounding air and so floats upwards. In the case of the landsurfer and the wind surfer, there is little friction on the surface, and the breeze forces them along.
Teachers' guide cross-references: Forces and movement, pages 13, 14, 42-3, 46, 111.

Down you go pages 22–3

Purpose: To convey two ideas: air resistance and gravity.
Note: In answer to the question in the box, explain to children that everything would fall at the same speed if air resistance did not slow things down.

Teachers' guide cross-references: Forces and movement, pages 46-8, 104.

Work it out pages 18–19

Purpose: To help children develop ideas about friction and forces and road safety.
Notes: The braking distances given here are taken from the Highway Code. Oil, which would greatly reduce friction, would extend the stopping distance as the car might not be able to brake at all, and could skid.
Extension activities: Look at the Highway Code to find out about how long it takes a car to stop in various conditions. Link this spread to the cycling proficiency test. Invite in a road safety officer.
Teachers' guide cross-references: Forces and movement, pages 56–61.

Building bridges pages 12–13

Purpose: To help children think about forces in balance.
Notes: The picture of the bridge with arrows only shows downward arrows – indicating that the structure is being pulled downwards by gravity. Ideally, it should also show upward arrows to show the up-thrust force.
Questions for discussion: Which is a suspension bridge? (Clifton Bridge – explain the term 'suspension bridge'.) When was the Tamar Bridge built? (The answer is on the bridge.) What does an engineer do? Discuss engineering as a job.
Extension activities: Starting with the bridges built by Brunel (Clifton and Tamar), make a history link to the Victorians. The class could make their own bridges and show the forces acting them.
Teachers' guide cross-references: Forces and movement, pages 90-1.

2.6 Planning your science programme in school

The following pages give examples of how two schools have planned their science programme for the whole of Key Stage 2. Planning of this kind helps to provide continuity and progression in children's learning in science. The development of such whole school programmes is discussed more fully in the *Science Co-ordinator's Handbook*.

Each plan covers the requirements for the National Curriculum at Key Stage 2 and shows which themes in the Nuffield Primary Science Teachers' Guides have been used for planning the topic in detail by the class teacher.

Example 1 (page 23)

Based in a semi-rural area this junior school has approximately 170 children on roll. There are no mixed age groups in the school. The plan provides for overlaps in order to provide opportunities for pupils to revisit concepts and build on their previous experience.

The overall curriculum is planned around topics which are history-led in the Autumn term, science-led in the Spring term and geography-led in the Summer term. Therefore, where ever possible cross-curricular links are developed, but if this becomes contrived, then subject specific mini-topics are planned. The programme only shows the Science elements taught each term.

Example 2 (page 24)

This urban school has recently reviewed its science programme in order to help encourage progression in the concepts covered and avoid repetition of the same activities. Teachers asked for guidance but also wanted the flexibility to develop the topics in a way which was appropriate to their own class.

It was also felt that some concepts, not necessarily demanded by the National Curriculum, should be covered e.g. Seasons. Therefore, suitable topics are included in the programme.

The summer term in Year 6 is free to accommodate SATs and to allow teachers time to further develop the interests of children.

Example 1

	AUTUMN TERM	**SPRING TERM**	**SUMMER TERM**
YEAR 3	The Earth and beyond/Magnetism	All about me	Service to our homes
Nuffield Primary Science Teachers' Guide	The Earth in Space 3.1, 3.2, 3.3 Electricity and magnetism 3.4	Living processes 3.1, 3.2, 3.3 The variety of life 3.2 Light 3.1	Electricity and magnetism 3.1, 3.2, 3.3 Materials 3.1 Using energy 3.2
Programme of Study †	Sc4:4a, b, c, d; Sc4:2a	Sc2: 1a; 2a, b, e, f; Sc4:3a, d	Sc3:1a, b, c; Sc4:1a, b, c
YEAR 4	Sound and music / Mechanisms	Habitats	Built environment
Nuffield Primary Science Teachers' Guide	Sound and music 3.1, 3.2 Using energy 3.3	The variety of life 3.1 Living processes 3.4 Living things in their environment 3.1, 3.2	Materials 3.2, 3.3 Using energy 3.1
Programme of Study †	Sc4:3e, f, g; Sc4:2d, e	Sc2:1b; 3a, b, c, d; 4a; Sc3:1d	Sc3:1e; 2a, b, c, d
YEAR 5	Electricity/Starting and stopping	Structures	Earth and atmosphere/Light
Nuffield Primary Science Teachers' Guide	Electricity and magnetism 3.2, 3.3 Forces and movement 3.1, 3.2	Materials 3.1, 3.2, 3.3 Rocks, soil and weather 3.1 The variety of life 3.3	Rocks, soil and weather 3.2 The Earth in Space 3.1, 3.2, 3.3, 3.4 Light 3.2, 3.3
Programme of Study †	Sc4:1a, b, c, d; Sc4:2b, c	Sc3:1b, d; 2f; 3a, b, c, d, e	Sc3:2e; Sc4:4a, b, c, d; Sc4:3a, b, c
YEAR 6	The human body/Keeping healthy	Forces	Our environment
Nuffield Primary Science Teachers' Guide	Living processes 3.2, 3.3 The variety of life 3.2	Forces and movement 3.1, 3.2, 3.3, 3.4 Electricity and magnetism 3.4 Using energy 3.3	Living things in their environment 3.2, 3.3, 3.4
Programme of Study †	Sc2:2c, d, g, h	Sc4:2a, b, c, d, e, f, g, h	Sc2:5a, b, c, d, e

† For the purposes of these charts the references to sections of the Programme of Study have been abbreviated as follows:
Sc2 = Life Processes and Living Things
Sc3 = Materials and their Properties
Sc4 = Physical Processes

Example 2

	AUTUMN TERM		SPRING TERM		SUMMER TERM	
YEAR 3	Earth and time	Reflections and shadows	What's under our feet?	Moving things	Variety of life	Habitats
Nuffield Primary Science Teachers' Guide	The Earth in Space 3.1, 3.2	Light 3.2	Rocks, soil and weather 3.1 Living things in their environment 3.3	Forces and movement 3.1	The variety of life 3.1	Living things in their environment 3.1
Programme of Study †	Sc4:4a, b, c, d	Sc4:3a, b, c	Sc2:5e; Sc3:1d	Sc4:2a, b, c, d, e	Sc2:1a, b; 4a	Sc2:5a, b
YEAR 4	Frictional forces	Hot and cold	Materials and their properties	Sounds	Growing	Electricity
Nuffield Primary Science Teachers' Guide	Forces and movement 3.2	Using energy 3.1	Materials 3.1	Sound and music 3.1	Living processes 3.1, 3.4	Electricity and magnetism 3.1, 3.2, 3.3
Programme of Study †	Sc4:2b, c, f, g, h	Sc3:2b, c	Sc3:1a, b, e	Sc4:3e, f	Sc2:3a, b, c, d	Sc3:1c; Sc4:1a, b, c
YEAR 5	The Earth in the Solar System	Weather and its effects	Feeding relationships	Individual variation	Light sources	Sounds travelling
Nuffield Primary Science Teachers' Guides	The Earth in Space 3.1, 3.2, 3.3	Rocks, soil and weather 3.1, 3.2	Living things in their environment 3.2, 3.3	The variety of life 3.2	Light 3.1	Sound and music 3.2
Programme of Study †	Sc4:c, d	Sc3:1d, 2e	Sc2:5c, d, e	Sc2:4a; 5a	Sc4:3a, b, c, d	Sc4:3e, f, g
YEAR 6	Forces and movement	Living processes	Electricity	Materials		
Nuffield Primary Science Teachers' Guide	Forces and movement 3.3, 3.4	Living processes 3.2, 3.3	Electricity and magnetism 3.1, 3.2, 3.3	Materials 3.2, 3.3		
Programme of Study †	Sc4:2d, e, f, g, h	Sc2:2a, b, c, d, e, f, g, h	Sc4:1c, d	Sc3:2a, b, d, f; 3a, b, c, d, e		

2.7 Resources

The precise nature of the resources needed at any time will, of course, depend upon the ideas that the children have and the methods of testing that they devise. However, the following list provides a general guide to the resources needed to carry out the investigations shown in this guide.

Ramps
Stop watches
Supports for ramps
Rulers and tapes
Toy cars and lorries
Aluminium foil
Bottles and cans (plastic)
Plasticine
Toy building bricks
Soft wood
Assorted materials (e.g. Lino, Corriflute, carpet tiles, carpet underlay)
Tools (if making, for instance, boats and/or trolleys for putting on slopes)
Dowling
Cotton reels
Balances
Elastic bands
Masses ('weights')
String
Newspapers
Sellotape
Drinking straws
Pins
Force meters

2.8 Warnings

 Activities which need particular care are indicated by this symbol in the margin. Everything possible should be done to ensure the safety of the children during their investigations. You should consult any guidelines produced by your school or LEA and if possible by CLEAPSS. See also the Association for Science Education publication *Be safe! some aspects of safety in school science and technology for Key Stages 1 and 2* (2nd edition, 1990). This contains more detailed advice than can be included here.

Particular care should be taken during work on *Forces and movement* because of the risk of injury resulting from moving objects and mechanisms and from using tools. In addition, investigations involving the dropping of objects require particular care. Injury can occur, not only because of a dropped object landing on someone but also as a result of children getting onto chairs, tables etc., to increase the dropping height.

Exploring forces and movement

Theme organizer

FORCES AND MOVEMENT

MOVING THINGS

Force is needed to change the movement of an object – to start it moving, speed it up, slow it down, stop it moving, or change its direction.

All things are pulled towards the centre of the Earth; it is a force called gravity which makes them fall.

*An object moving at a steady speed in a straight line is being acted on by balanced forces.

STOPPING AND STAYING PUT

Force is needed to change the movement of an object – to start it moving, speed it up, slow it down, stop it moving, or change its direction.

Friction is a force which opposes the movement of one surface across another.

*If an object is stationary it is being acted on by balanced forces.

FLOATING AND SINKING

Some objects float in water but others sink.

Whether or not something floats depends on a combination of factors, which include the material it is made of, its shape, and the liquid it is in.

*When something floats the forces acting on it are balanced.

*A material will float if its density is less than, or equal to, the density of the liquid it is in.

STRUCTURES AND BALANCE

All things are pulled towards the centre of the Earth; it is a force called gravity which makes them fall.

Forces can change the shape of objects.

*Stable/balanced objects are being acted on by balanced forces.

*An object is most stable when its centre of mass is as low as possible.

(*Asterisks indicate ideas which will be developed more fully in later key stages.)

Moving things

AREAS FOR INVESTIGATION

◆ Experience of movement of a variety of things on land and water and in the air.

◆ Factors affecting the movement of objects.

KEY IDEAS

◆ Force is needed to change the movement of an object – to start it moving, speed it up, slow it down, stop it moving, or change its direction.

◆ All things are pulled towards the centre of the Earth; it is a force called gravity which makes them fall.

◆ *An object moving at a steady speed in a straight line is being acted on by balanced forces.

(*Asterisks indicate ideas which will be developed more fully in later key stages.)

A LOOK AT
moving things

Pushing, pulling, twisting and squeezing are all actions which involve the use of forces. A push or pull is needed to make a stationary object move. A push or pull can also cause a moving object to move faster or to swerve, changing its direction. Pushes and pulls can also make moving objects slow down and stop.

Starting, speeding up, slowing down and stopping all involve changes in the speed of an object. Speed relates distance to time: it indicates the distance covered in a certain time. A car moving at 30 miles per hour would cover 30 miles in one hour if it continued to move at that same speed (or 15 miles in half an hour, and so on). Putting it precisely, speed equals distance divided by time.

The bigger the force, the greater its effect on changes in the movement of an object. Changes in an object's movement are also affected by the direction of forces acting on it. A moving ball struck from behind by a blow in the same direction as it is moving will speed up in that direction. If it is struck a glancing blow from behind, it will also change direction.

Objects fall because they are being pulled towards the centre of the Earth. This pull is the force called gravity. When an object (such as a toy car) goes down a slope, part of its movement is vertically downwards. Gravity is the cause of this movement.

Finding out children's ideas

■ STARTER ACTIVITIES

1 Identifying things that move

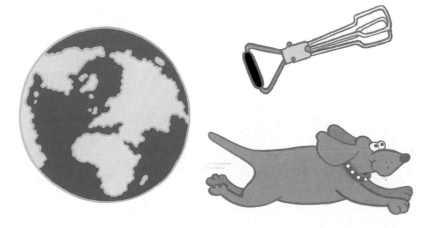

Ask children to collect pictures of things which move and arrange them as a collage to form the focus for a discussion.

Q *What do you think makes these things move?*

From your children's answers you can build up a general picture of what they see as causes of movement - see the 'Children's ideas' section on page 33.

2 Moving down a slope

Q *See what happens if you let the car run down the slope. What do you think makes the car move?*
Tell me about how the car moves on the slope.
What do you think makes this happen?
What happens if you try to get the car to go up the slope?

Let the children play with cars and ramps, then encourage them to put their ideas down on an annotated drawing.

3 Moving a boat through water

Get the children to bring a selection of small toy boats which can be floated in a tank of water. Ask children to make the boats move in as many different ways as possible. Challenge them to move a boat without touching it. Then they can draw or write down their ideas about how and why the boat moves.

Q *What do you think the boat needs to make it move? What do you think is happening when you push the boat?*

4 Throwing

Let children spend time exploring what happens to things they throw – balls, beanbags, etc. This should be done in carefully controlled conditions, probably in the playground. They can try throwing in different ways:

◆ straight up as far as possible;
◆ as far away as possible.

Then they can record their observations in drawings, showing what happens to the ball from the start of the throw to the time it stops moving. Ask them to write on the drawings why the ball acts in the way it does.

Q *Why do you think the ball moves in that way? Why do you think the ball comes back down to the ground?*

5 Paper spinners or gliders

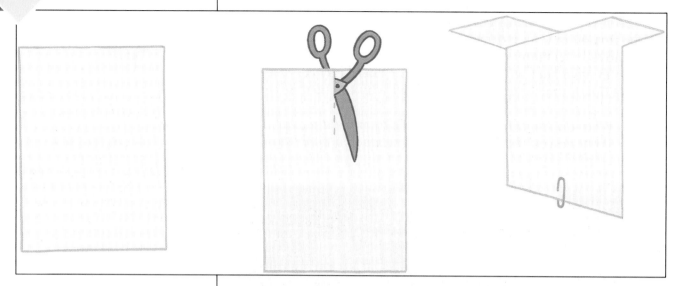

Get the children to design and make paper spinners. This illustration shows a possible design. If a range of designs are used the activity should not be treated as a competition. At this stage children should not focus on which moves best but rather on what happens. While children are dropping a spinner, they could be asked about its performance.

What do we need to do to make it move?
What is the shape of its flight path?
How would you describe the way it comes down to the ground?
What do you think makes it come down?

Alternatively, make paper gliders. A possible design is illustrated below, but children may well have their own ideas about how to make them.

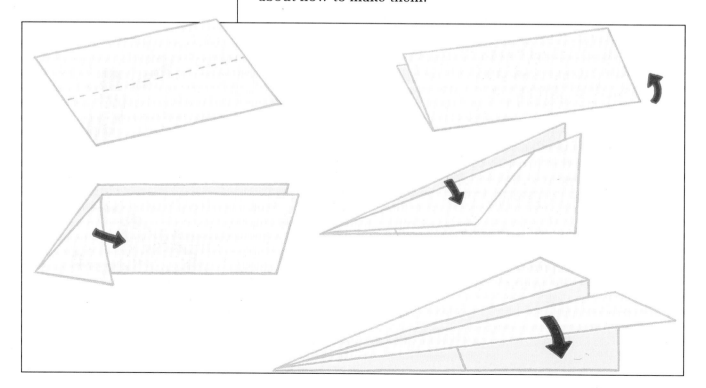

Children's ideas

Children's attempts to explain their observations of moving things reveal a wide range of ideas. Some of these are presented in this section, which forms an overview of the ideas that many children express when considering movement and forces. Nevertheless, it is important that you find out the beliefs your children themselves have. You may find that they share some of the ideas presented here, or that their beliefs are quite different.

Ideas about moving things

Young children recognize movement in many things, for example humans, vehicles and animals.

Older children have an increased range including the Sun, Moon, clouds and the Earth itself.

Children may express the idea that a moving object has an in-built ability to move. No reason is given to explain why this is so – it just goes!

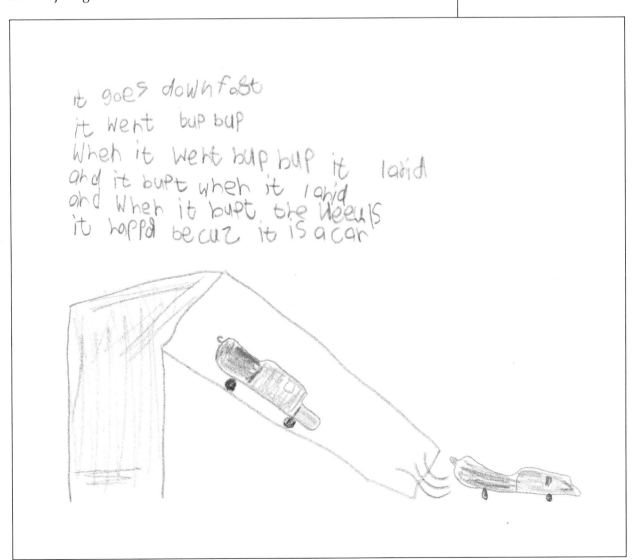

it goes down fast
it went bup bup
When it went bup bup it land
and it bupt when it land
and When it bupt the weeuls
it happd becuz it is a car

Other children refer to parts of the moving object and give these as the cause of the movement.

A car moves because of its wheels.
A boat moves because of its oars.
A bird moves because of its wings.
People move because of their legs.

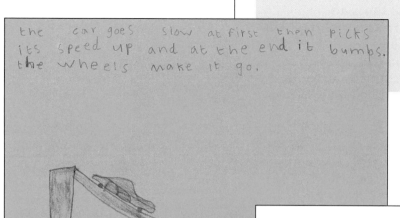

the car goes slow at first then picks its speed up and at the end it bumps. the wheels make it go.

1. It falls down car the slope
2. The wheels make it roll down the slope.

Other features of the moving object may be picked out. Shape, speed and direction are sometimes used to explain the movement, but the most common attribute given is 'weight'.

car it rolls down the slop Because of the weight on the wheels.

In their responses to the slope activity, some children said the car moved because of the slope. Others gave more precise reasons – the steepness of the slope or the slippery surface.

The toy Car

The car went down the slope and the wheels rolled I think it did this because the slope was slanted.

All of the examples given on the previous page are valid responses to the question: What makes a particular object move?

However, they give no indication that a force is bringing about the movement.

Some children may recognize that a force is needed to move an object. They may describe it as a push or a pull.

> *You can pull, push or blow a toy car to make it move. If you put a car on a slope, the slope is taking the place of a push.*

Some children will explain the downward movement of objects on a slope in terms of gravity.

> *The car went down the ramp. Gravity pulls the car down.*

Ideas about falling

Many children consider that things fall because they are released or let go. The figure shows how one child put it.

Unlike 'going up', which needs the force of a throw, 'coming down' is regarded as a natural event that just happens; it does not require a force from a person to make it happen.

Other children may pick out weight as an important feature. This is what one child who had been throwing up a ball said.

> *It comes down fast because it's a little bit heavy. It can't go up and up because it isn't dead light. I had to throw it up. If I put it on my hand and said, 'Up', it wouldn't go.*

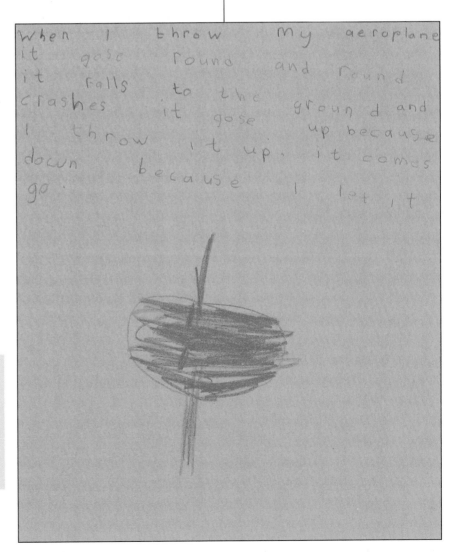

When I throw my aeroplane it gose round and round it falls to the ground and crashes it gose up because I throw it up. it comes down because I let it go.

Such children attribute the falling of the ball to its heaviness (just as heaviness is often given as the reason for things sinking in water). According to the child, the ball is 'a little bit heavy' and therefore it falls quickly. Does this imply that the heavier something is the more quickly it will fall? Certainly this is the expectation of a great number of children.

Children have often heard of gravity and give it as their idea for why things fall.

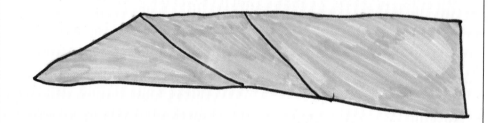

Adele Roberts   March 23rd

Paper Aeroplane

First I threw the aeroplane into the air. It went straight forward at first and then it curved and fell down onto the floor.
The nose of the aeroplane got a bit bashed when it landed on the floor. The reason why it went on the floor is gravity.

Different ideas can be held about gravity itself.

The ball falls down because it's heavy. Gravity pulls it down. It's like drops of air but you can't see it.

It is not clear from this statement how far the child has associated weight (heaviness) with gravity. But clearly gravity has been linked with air. In this case gravity has been regarded as pulling things down. Other children have described it as pushing down on things.

Some children give air as a cause for things falling while others see it as doing the opposite – keeping things up. Similar comments have been made about wind. Compare these two ideas from different children.

I threw the ball up and it went down. The wind made it come down.

If I threw it up hard into the sky, it would stay up. The wind would keep it up.

The next example is from a child who has ideas about opposing forces in a flying plane.

> # Why a paper aeroplane flies
>
> cutting through air easily
>
> side veiw
>
> air pressure under wing
>
> When you throw a paper plane it obviously goes up, across and down. There is Gravity and air pressure acting on this plane. The "wing" traps air underneath, so helping it to stay in the sky. Gravity is stopping the plane just going up and away. The nose cone is slim and cuts through the air easily. As in the ball, as the push wears off, the plane comes down.

The downwards pull of gravity (which stops it going up) is opposed by the upwards push of air under the wings (which stops it coming down). This is clearly a sophisticated idea.

It is worth noting, however, that in the child's last sentence a 'push that wears off' is mentioned. In other words, the child believes that the initial force to get an object moving remains in that object and decreases as it slows down. This intuitive idea is not the scientific view (see 'Background science', Chapter 5).

Helping children to develop their ideas

The chart opposite shows how you can help children to develop their ideas from starting points which have given rise to different ideas.

The centre rectangle contains a starter question.

The surrounding 'thought bubbles' contain the sorts of ideas expressed by children.

The further ring of rectangles contains questions posed by teachers in response to the ideas expressed by the children. These questions are meant to prompt children to think about their ideas.

The outer ovals indicate ways in which the children might respond to the teacher's questions.

Some of the shapes have been left blank, as a sign that other ideas may be encountered and other ways of helping children to develop their ideas may be tried.

All the activities given in this section are closely linked to those on stopping objects moving, described in 'Stopping and staying put' (page 50).

1 Playing with toys

Children begin to develop their ideas on the effects of forces on moving things by playing with toy cars, balls and other objects which move. Their play should be directed through questions which will focus their observations on specific things. For example:

Helping children to develop their ideas about moving things

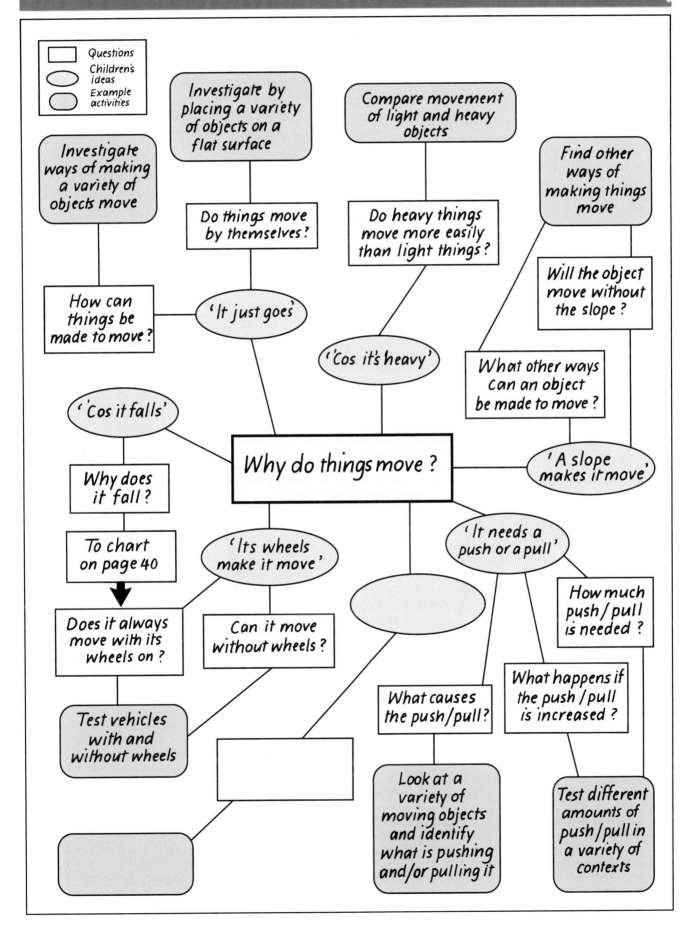

Questions

Children's ideas

Example activities

Investigate by placing a variety of objects on a flat surface

Compare movement of light and heavy objects

Investigate ways of making a variety of objects move

Find other ways of making things move

Do things move by themselves?

Do heavy things move more easily than light things?

How can things be made to move?

'It just goes'

Will the object move without the slope?

''Cos it's heavy'

What other ways can an object be made to move?

''Cos it falls'

Why does it fall?

Why do things move?

'A slope makes it move'

To chart on page 40

'Its wheels make it move'

'It needs a push or a pull'

How much push/pull is needed?

Does it always move with its wheels on?

Can it move without wheels?

What happens if the push/pull is increased?

Test vehicles with and without wheels

What causes the push/pull?

Look at a variety of moving objects and identify what is pushing and/or pulling it

Test different amounts of push/pull in a variety of contexts

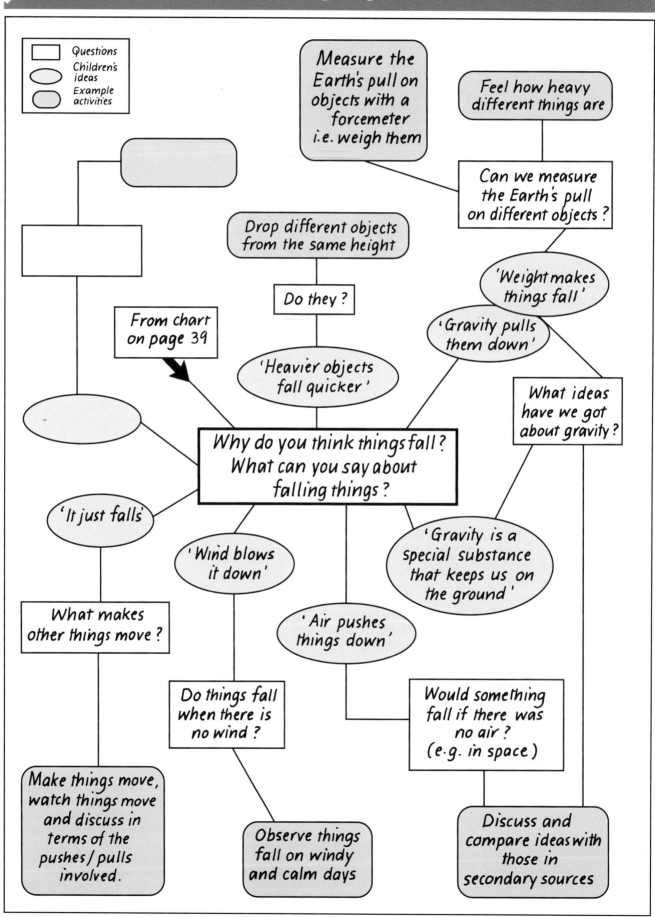

Questions
Children's ideas
Example activities

Measure the Earth's pull on objects with a forcemeter i.e. weigh them

Feel how heavy different things are

Can we measure the Earth's pull on different objects?

Drop different objects from the same height

Do they?

From chart on page 39

'Weight makes things fall'

'Gravity pulls them down'

'Heavier objects fall quicker'

What ideas have we got about gravity?

Why do you think things fall? What can you say about falling things?

'It just falls'

'Wind blows it down'

'Gravity is a special substance that keeps us on the ground'

'Air pushes things down'

What makes other things move?

Do things fall when there is no wind?

Would something fall if there was no air? (e.g. in space)

Make things move, watch things move and discuss in terms of the pushes/pulls involved.

Observe things fall on windy and calm days

Discuss and compare ideas with those in secondary sources

Q *What effect do pushes of different strengths have on the car?*
What happens if a moving car is given an extra push?
What happens if the push is not directly behind the car?
How can the car be made to change direction?
Can you find a way of making the car move without pushing it directly with your hand?

While playing with toys provides direct experience of the effects of forces on moving objects, more systematic investigations should also be developed.

PUSHES AND PULLS CAN MAKE AN OBJECT MOVE, SPEED UP, OR CHANGE DIRECTION

2 Moving on a flat surface

One group of children developed an investigation into moving on a flat surface, using the arrangement shown.

They devised a fair test to compare the effects of the same push (pulling the elastic back the same distance each time) on different cars. They agreed that they would record the distance travelled by measuring from where the back of the car started to where it finished, along the coloured strip they used as their track.

! CARE IS NEEDED IN USING ELASTIC BANDS

AT 1 PLANNING AND CARRYING OUT FAIR TESTS

e

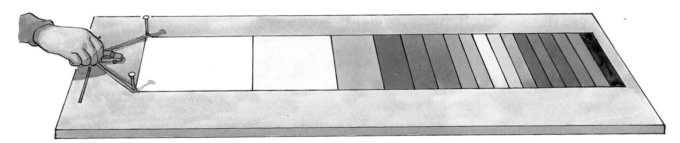

This arrangement could also be used to investigate:

◆ the effects of different forces on the same car – the force of the elastic could be measured with a force meter like this.

t THE GREATER THE FORCE, THE GREATER THE DISTANCE THE SAME CAR WILL TRAVEL

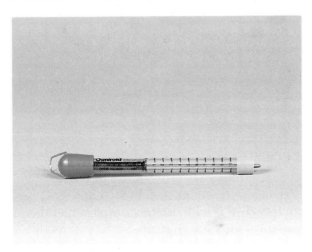

Force meter (spring balance)

◆ the effects of different surfaces on the distance travelled (see also 'Stopping and staying put', page 50).

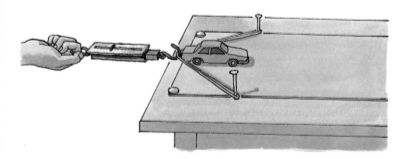

Measuring the force

AT
1   INTERPRETING RESULTS
     AND FINDINGS

Results for these investigations could be presented in graphs or tables. Children would then be able to look for patterns and relationships in their findings.

 Does the distance travelled increase with a bigger push?
Does the car travel further on a smooth surface?
Do different cars travel different distances?
Can you make the car travel up a slope?
What effect does the slope have on the distance travelled? Why does this happen?

Some children may wish to consider the effects of pushing and throwing things in relation to playground games such as those described in *Forces and movement*.

3 Moving down a slope

As an extension of the starter activity (page 30), cars and other objects (such as bottles, balls, cans, and toy bricks of different shapes and sizes) can be compared as they move down slopes set up at various angles.

The investigations are very similar to those shown in 'Moving on a flat surface' (page 41) because the slope is simply being used to get the objects moving. There is an opportunity here for children to make predictions which they can then test.

They can compare the movement of different objects.

 Do large balls roll further than small balls?

They can find the effects of raising and lowering the slope.

 Does a steeper slope always make the object roll further?

And they can investigate the effects of different surfaces such as sandpaper, polished wood and carpet. (See also 'Stopping and staying put', page 50.)

Children often want to measure the effects on the object by recording the time taken to reach a particular point. However, they soon appreciate the difficulty of measuring short times, and turn to measuring the distances travelled.

Problem-solving activities can develop from these investigations. Challenge the children to design and make a car which would travel exactly 2 metres from the bottom of the ramp. Achieving this will engage them in manipulating the variables involved.

e

 MEASURING

4 Making movement easier

Children recognize that vehicles which have wheels move more easily than those without.

They can compare wheeled and wheel-less vehicles.

 REDUCING THE AMOUNT OF SURFACE CONTACT MAKES MOVEMENT EASIER

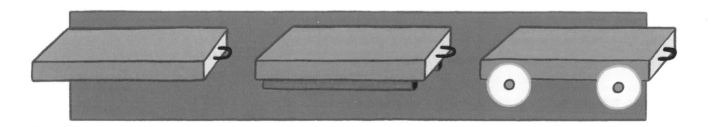

To do this, they should construct three simple vehicles, and use a force meter to measure the force required to move them, loaded and unloaded, over different surfaces. (See also 'Stopping and staying put', page 50.)

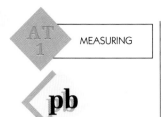

pb

Encourage the children to discuss the advantages and disadvantages of each vehicle.

The pictures of different types of wheel in *Forces and movement* can be used to stimulate further discussion about the use of wheels.

5 Making sailing boats

The effects of forces on moving objects can be investigated by exploring the movement of boats. Children could first discuss any experience they have of sailing boats.

Let the children make simple sailing boats, either to their own design or like those shown here.

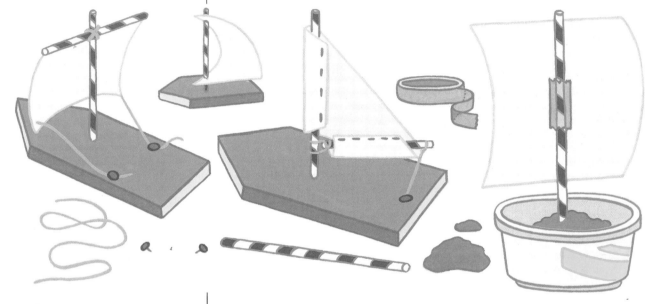

They can test what happens when the 'wind' comes from different directions.

To provide the 'wind' use a bicycle pump, balloon inflater or battery-operated fan.

Children can modify the designs of their boats and discuss how well these perform in relation to the pushes/pulls involved.

Q *What is the best size/shape for the sail?*
What is the best shape for the hull?

Boats will probably capsize, which can lead to a discussion of balance and stability. (See 'Structures and balance', page 76).

Q *Why do you think the boat capsized?*
What could you do to make it more difficult for the boat to capsize?

Pictures of the wind-surfer and land-yacht in *More about forces and movement* can be used for further discussion.

! DO NOT USE AN ELECTRIC HAIR-DRYER – DANGER OF ELECTROCUTION IF IT GETS WET OR FALLS IN THE WATER

t THE MOVEMENT OF AN OBJECT DEPENDS ON THE SIZE AND DIRECTION OF THE FORCES ACTING ON IT

pb

6 Testing hulls and moving loads

Explore movement in water using bowls and fish tanks. A long trough can extend the scope of investigations. A large, deep trough is ideal but is not always available. The substitute shown in the diagram is easy to make.

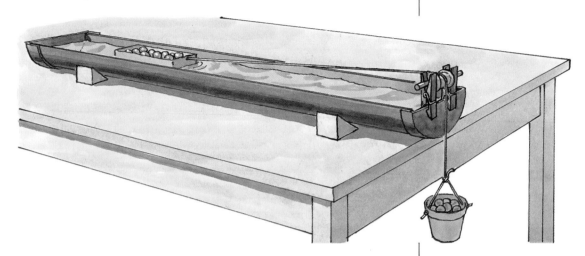

This set-up makes an extensive range of investigations possible. One way to help children to understand how forces can be measured is to ask:

 Q *How many marbles have to be put in the cup to move the boat?*
What happens when the pull on the boat is increased?
What is the result of increasing the load in the boat?
What is the effect of changing the shape of the hull?

Forces and movement shows different types of boat; it also looks at the Plimsoll line which shows how much cargo has been put into a boat.

 t THE LARGER THE FORCE ON AN OBJECT, THE MORE QUICKLY IT INCREASES ITS SPEED. GREATER LOADS REQUIRE GREATER FORCES TO MOVE THEM

 pb

7 Elastic band powered vehicles

Cars and boats can be powered by elastic bands. Vehicles driven in this way provide scope for many investigations, as well as a link with ideas on energy (see the Using energy teachers' guide, page 79).

 ! CARE IS NEEDED IN USING ELASTIC BANDS

Making boats with 'paddles', similar to the one shown here, provides scope for:

◆ discussion of the pushes involved;
◆ investigations of the relationship between the number of turns given to the elastic and the distance travelled.

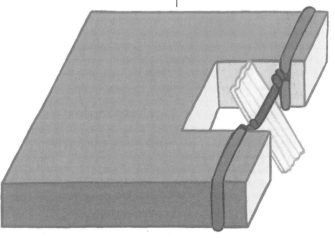

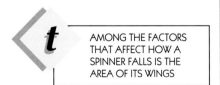

AMONG THE FACTORS THAT AFFECT HOW A SPINNER FALLS IS THE AREA OF ITS WINGS

Encourage children to find examples of other ways in which things can be made to move. *Forces and movement* and *More about forces and movement* both provide examples which might be discussed.

8 Talking about pushes and pulls

During children's work on forces and movement they will use both everyday and technical words to explain their ideas. Many will use 'pushes' and 'pulls' to explain forces acting on moving objects. Starting with pushes and pulls as they occur in the playground, they can think about everyday events, and collect instances where pushes and pulls occur and record them in diagrams or in a logbook.

There are many everyday experiences which involve pushes and pulls. You could use the pictures in *Forces and movement* and *More about forces and movement* to provide stimuli for discussion. Children may write a story or poem about them. *More about forces and movement* gives examples.

9 Things that fall

Children's ideas about falling can be developed by extending the starter activities on paper spinners (or gliders) and other falling objects. This gives children the opportunity to put forward ideas about factors that affect how things fall. There will be many opportunities during the testing of those ideas for the development of process skills. The interaction that takes place during such activities also allows children to discuss and challenge one another's ideas.

Use the examples in *Forces and movement* and *More about forces and movement* to help children think about why some things fall and others do not.

The following two activities allow children to explore their ideas about how things fall and the factors which affect movement through the air. The experiences gained from these activities will be useful for the next section, which focuses on ideas about *why* things fall.

a Paper spinners or gliders

Encourage children to make spinners which differ from each other in one respect only. Spinners could vary in the size or shape of their wings, or their weight.

They can use pieces of card of the same size to make spinners with wings of different sizes but the same shape.

Then they can predict which one will fall most quickly and carry out a test.

Q *What has to be kept the same to make this fair?*
Dropping it from the same height?
Releasing rather than giving it a push?
Dropping all the spinners at the same time?

AT 1   PLANNING AND
CARRYING OUT FAIR
TESTS

Alternatively, children can carry out similar investigations
with paper gliders, made to different designs. In this case, it is
difficult in practice to make a test flight a fair one. But children
might like to consider these questions:

Q *How can you give each glider the same push?*
How can you throw each one at the same angle?
*Can you make sure that the test is not spoilt by different
draughts or winds?*

Children can, at least, become aware of what they are trying to
keep the same. They should also discuss how they will
compare the flights and what can be measured.

b Balls and other falling objects

t   HEAVIER AND LIGHTER
BALLS FALL AT THE SAME
RATE (PROVIDED THAT
THEIR AIR RESISTANCE IS
THE SAME)

Focus on how balls fall by
dropping rather than
throwing them. Many
children are likely to
predict that a heavier ball
will fall faster than a
lighter one. To test this,
release pairs of balls of
different weights at the
same time from the same
height, preferably 3 metres
or more.

Other pairs of objects
could be tested in the same
way – a small pebble and a
big stone, for example.
Some children may not

!   CHILDREN MUST TAKE
CARE WHEN DROPPING
THINGS FROM A HEIGHT

think that objects of different size or mass will hit the ground at the same time. Encourage repeated and careful observation.

Q *How did you manage to drop two things at exactly the same time from exactly the same height?*

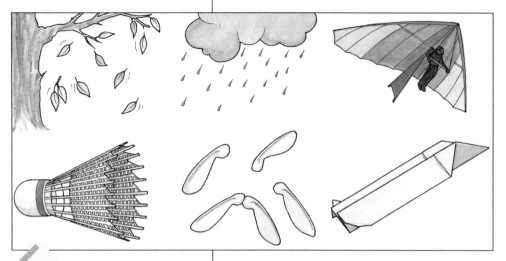

The children can make a collection of different things that fall (the real thing or pictures).

They can watch some of these things fall.

Then they can discuss why many things fall at the same rate, while others fall more slowly.

t THE FALL OF SOME OBJECTS IS SLOWED DOWN BY THEIR SHAPE, WHICH INCREASES THEIR AIR RESISTANCE

AT 1 PLANNING AND CARRYING OUT FAIR TESTS

t OBJECTS FALL BECAUSE THEY ARE PULLED TOWARDS THE CENTRE OF THE EARTH

If children raise the question of slowing a fall down, take the opportunity to look at parachutes.

Compare different designs (shapes, holes, sizes, number of strings) using fair tests.

10   Why things fall

The previous activities with spinners and balls give children plenty of experience of falling objects. Falling is an event which occurs without an obvious push or pull. Children may not associate it with any kind of force.

If they do not connect falling with a force, use and discuss other instances when objects move.

Q *How can you move this ball along level ground?*
Can you make it move without pushing or pulling it in some way?
Is there a push or pull when the ball moves downwards – falls?

It is common for some children in a class to have heard of gravity and to give it as an explanation for things falling.

If children seem familiar with the word 'gravity', discuss what it means to them. Ask children where they have heard the word before and what ideas they have about it. Try to find out if they recognize it as a 'pull' – that is, a force.

V

Let children find examples of gravity in action, and perhaps draw pictures to illustrate them. Discuss these instances to encourage children to apply the concept of gravity more generally. For example:

Q *If gravity is what makes an object fall straight down, is it also what makes an object such as a paper glider, lose height gradually?*
Is it what makes an object roll down a slope (for example, a toy car)?
If gravity makes an object fall through the air, is it also what makes something sink in water?
Is it also what holds down a stationary object, so that it does not just drift away?

 t GRAVITY IS THE FORCE PULLING THINGS TOWARDS THE EARTH'S CENTRE

Use 'imagination' exercises such as those below to help children reveal and develop their ideas.

They can write down and then discuss what would happen if the Earth's gravity were suddenly reduced.

Q *What would happen if people went down a hole drilled through the Earth?*

Use the pictures and information in *Forces and movement* and *More about forces and movement* to discuss questions such as this.

 pb

Ask children to draw the Earth as it looks from space, and add people living in different places and some clouds with rain falling. Children's drawings may look like the left-hand picture below rather than the right-hand one. Discuss the different pictures to help develop the notion of gravity acting towards the centre of the Earth. (See *The Earth in Space*.)

Compare children's ideas with actual scientific explanations. For example, they may believe that, because things dropped from a height reach a high speed, gravity increases as you get higher up. Then try to get the children to compare the explanations given by their ideas with the scientific explanations.

 t EVERYTHING IS ATTRACTED TOWARDS THE CENTRE OF THE EARTH BY GRAVITY. GRAVITY DOES NOT INCREASE WITH HEIGHT ABOVE THE EARTH – IT GRADUALLY DECREASES

To gain experience of the different force with which the Earth pulls on different objects, they can lift objects and feel how heavy they are, or measure the pulls more accurately with force meters. This may help in establishing the link between gravity and weight.

 t THE WEIGHT OF AN OBJECT IS A MEASURE OF HOW HARD THE EARTH IS PULLING ON IT

Stopping and staying put

AREAS FOR INVESTIGATION

◆ The ways in which a moving object can be stopped.

◆ The forces needed to stop objects moving at different speeds.

◆ The effects of different surfaces on moving objects.

The activities in this section are closely linked to those described in 'Moving things' (page 28), but here the emphasis is on what makes an object stop or stand still.

KEY IDEAS

◆ Force is needed to change the movement of an object – to start it moving, speed it up, slow it down, stop it moving, or change its direction.

◆ Friction is a force which opposes the movement of one surface across another.

◆ *If an object is stationary it is being acted on by balanced forces.

(*Asterisks indicate ideas which will be developed more fully in later key stages.)

A LOOK AT
stopping and staying put

A force is a push or pull. Pushes and pulls can make a stationary object move.

A small push may not be enough to slide a box along the ground. This is because there is another force appearing to 'hold' the box when you try to move it. This 'gripping' force acts in the opposite direction to that in which the push would make it move.

The force which pushes in a direction opposite to the expected movement is called friction. The frictional force is greater if the surface is rough than if it is smooth. It would, for example, be harder to start the box moving on carpet than it would on lino.

The box would slide down a slope only if the slope were steep enough. On gentler slopes the frictional force is sufficient to prevent the box from moving.

As well as helping things to stay put, frictional forces can also make moving objects slow down and stop. The greater the frictional force, the more quickly a moving object will stop and the shorter the distance it will stop in. Shoes and tyres with a good tread are more effective if you want to stop quickly and without skidding, because having a tread increases the roughness of the surface. The braking distance of a moving vehicle is longer if it is moving faster because a larger force is needed to stop it.

Frictional forces are not the only ones that stop objects moving. A direct push or pull can act in the opposite direction to movement, as happens when a moving vehicle runs into a barrier and is stopped by the barrier pushing on it.

Finding out children's ideas

STARTER ACTIVITIES

Some of the starter activities given in 'Moving things' (page 28), can also be used to reveal children's ideas about why objects stop. Ask questions which help the children think about 'stopping' rather than 'moving'.

1 Slowing down and stopping

Children could either allow toy cars to run down a slope or give them a push on a level surface. Focus their attention on the slowing down and stopping of the car rather than what makes it start moving.

 What do you think makes the car stop?
Why do you think the car slows down?
How else could you get the car to stop?
How could you get the car to stop more quickly?

2 Staying put

If the children have previously done some work with cars going down slopes, before placing a block of wood on a slope ask:

 What do you think will happen if I put this block on the slope?

Ask the children to explain the reasons for their response.

Then put the block on the slope and ask the children:

 Why do you think the block stays where it is?
Can you think of anything that is stopping it from moving?
How might you get the block to move on the slope?
Can you make it move in any other way?
What do you think makes it move in that direction?
Is there anything stopping it moving in the opposite direction?

The inclusion of some questions which refer to moving the block helps to find out what the child thinks is preventing the block from moving, that is, what is making it stay put.

Children's ideas

Not surprisingly, children's ideas about what makes things stop moving show some similarity to their ideas about why things move. But it is probably harder for them to recognize that some kind of force is involved in stopping since, in many cases, no obvious push is involved.

Young children may relate the stopping of an object to how they feel when they want to stop. These remarks show this:

> *It gets tired.*
> *It's been a long way.*

Or they may suggest that it is the same reason as it could be in certain circumstances for the real object. For example, a car was referred to here:

> *It's run out of petrol.*

Many children do recognize that something is stopping things moving. They express this idea in different ways. The following comment refers to the lack of slope.

> The car stops because it hasn't got a slope to go down.

Other children will combine the lack of slope with a property of the object, for instance 'weight' and 'wheels'.

> The car stop because it is not on a slont and the wheels sterp.

> ②. why does it stop. it stops because it is no longer on a slope and its weight

These quotations from discussions refer to the idea of gripping and sticking:

> *You need grip for the car to stay still on the hill.*

> *If you put the car sideways on the ramp it won't go down because the grip holds it there.*

The children are clearly expressing the idea of friction but as yet do not name it as such.

Many children have the intuitive idea of 'push' as an entity which remains in the object and is slowly lost. This is in conflict with the scientific explanation, and is discussed further in 'Background science' (Chapter 5).

why does it stop. ans the force from the push were's down.

Some children introduce words such as 'power' and 'energy':

> *The cars do not move on their own because there is no power behind them.*
>
> *It stops when it bumps into something or if it runs out of the energy your fingers give it when you push it.*

The last examples show the beginnings of ideas about the relation of force and energy. It is very unlikely that children of primary age will be able to make the necessary distinctions, but they should be given a wide range of situations in which they can begin to identify the forces involved in stopping.

Helping children to develop their ideas

The chart opposite shows how you can help children to develop their ideas from starting points which have given rise to different ideas.

The centre rectangles contain starter questions.

The surrounding 'thought bubbles' contain the sorts of ideas expressed by children.

The further ring of rectangles contains questions posed by teachers in response to the ideas expressed by the children. These questions are meant to prompt children to think about their ideas.

The outer ovals indicate ways in which the children might respond to the teacher's questions.

Some of the shapes have been left blank, as a sign that other ideas may be encountered and other ways of helping children to develop their ideas may be tried.

The activities described here complement those given in 'Moving things' (page 28) and are intended to emphasize the factors involved when an object slows down and stops. Much of the emphasis relies on the nature of the questions asked and the way in which the activity is presented.

1 Stopping ourselves

It is not easy to carry out precise investigations involving human movement, but it is possible to experience some of the effects of stopping. For example, one class spent some of its PE time on stopping and starting.

The children looked at:

THE GREATER THE SPEED, THE HARDER IT IS TO STOP – IT REQUIRES MORE FORCE

- ◆ the difference between stopping from a walk, a jog, and a run at full speed – one child performed the movements while another gave the command 'stop' and attempted to estimate how far the first child then moved;

- ◆ the effect of different footwear: bare feet, socks, shoes with smooth soles and trainers with treads – the same child used the various kinds of footwear moving at the same speed on the same surface until commanded to stop;

WARN ABOUT ACCIDENTS CAUSED BY SLIPPING, ESPECIALLY ON WET FLOOR

- ◆ the effects of surfaces: slippery (polished floor), rough (playground), soft (sand on beach), and grass – the same footwear was worn by the same child on the different surfaces.

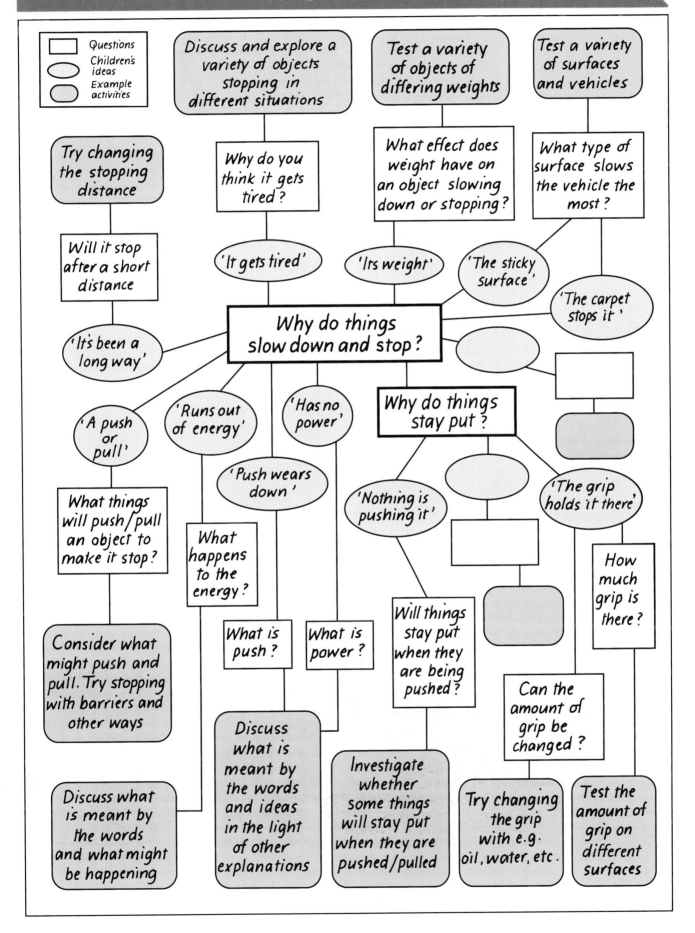

STATIONARY OBJECTS
ARE ACTED ON BY EQUAL
AND OPPOSING FORCES

You could use the pictures in *Forces and movement* to provide further examples of the effects of footwear and the grip they provide. Encourage the children to discuss why the soles of the shoes are different.

It is also possible for children to experience the fact that pushes and pulls (forces) can exist when little or no movement takes place.

2 Stopping things moving

a Barriers

The most obvious ways of stopping an object are:

◆ to put a barrier in its path;
◆ to pull or push in the opposite direction.

AT 1
PLANNING AND
CARRYING OUT FAIR
TESTS

Work with toy cars and a ramp to investigate the effects of different barriers on a moving vehicle. Encourage children to:

◆ design their investigation;
◆ make predictions;
◆ use a fair test;
◆ record their results and draw conclusions.

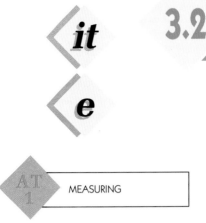

If a video camcorder is available, you could use this to record and then analyse the events at impact.

Use different materials, such as various kinds of plastic foam, wood, metal and cotton wool. Record the performance of the barrier through observation or by measuring the distance the vehicle bounces off it.

Develop alternative ways of measuring the performance of the barrier. Two possibilities might be:

♦ to measure the distance the barrier is moved by the car at impact;
♦ to design a method for measuring the extent to which a fixed barrier is deformed by the car.

 MEASURING

Questions which can help children think about what is actually causing the vehicle to stop might include:

Q *What do you think the barrier is doing to stop the car?*
Can you suggest why some materials stop the car better than others?
What do you think a good barrier should do?
Why is it that some barriers might not stop the car?
What happens when the car is moving faster?

Children can try to find out about the design and performance of real crash barriers by contacting road safety organizations.

b Slowing down and stopping

Children watching a car go down a ramp will realize that it will stop eventually even when there is no barrier in the way. If asked, they will be able to suggest reasons for this. Two ideas which were investigated by groups of children are:

 THE FASTER THE CAR THE GREATER THE DISTANCE IT TAKES TO STOP

i The effect of increased speed on stopping distance

Q *Do cars travelling faster go further before stopping?*

 COMMUNICATING

This activity provides an excellent opportunity for children to record their results as a table and then present them in graph form to show the relationship of one variable with another.

ii The effect of the surface over which the car is travelling

Q *Do some surfaces slow the car down more quickly than others?*

Different materials, such as sandpaper, carpet or lino can be laid on the slope and/or at the bottom of it.

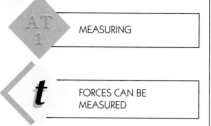

AT 1 — MEASURING

t — FORCES CAN BE MEASURED

3 How much grip?

Some children may be starting to think about quantified investigations of friction. The following shows how children might measure the force required to move an object over a surface – or, put negatively, the force that is stopping an object from being moved.

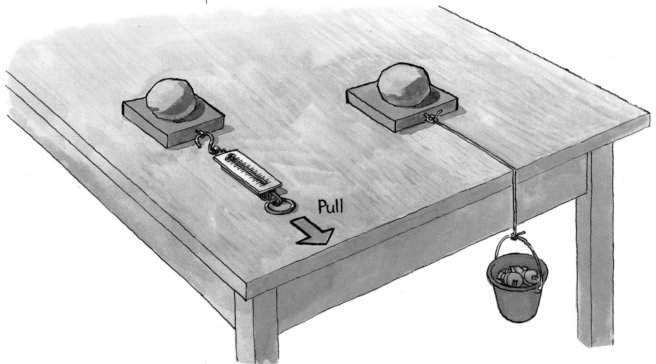

Pull

Q *Which types of surface have the most 'grip' (that is, create the most friction)?*
How can this be overcome?

! CHILDREN MUST NOT LOOK AT THE TREAD PATTERNS ON CAR TYRES WHEN THE CAR IS ON A ROAD

t — ICE, WATER AND OIL ACT TO REDUCE FRICTION

e   **pb**

For a variation on this activity, start with the children looking at car and bicycle tyres and the tread patterns. Record the patterns by making rubbings or prints of them. You may be able to collect pieces of tyre and attach them to the block of wood (instead of the other materials) so that they can be tested in the same way. Relate this to the effects of ice, water, and oil on roads. Children should consider the importance of adequate tread on car and bicycle tyres for road safety.

If it is difficult to look at actual car tyres, the children could look at the pictures in *Forces and movement.*

More about forces and movement provides information about braking distances and children could use these as part of their discussion.

4 Examples of friction

Let the children discuss the reasons for their findings about slowing down and stopping. It is likely that children will use words such as 'grip', 'stick' or 'hold' to describe their ideas about friction. Relate the findings to practical matters such as road surfaces, vehicles stopping at road junctions and the braking distances of vehicles travelling at different speeds.

In the following questions, use the word for friction that the children themselves use, and introduce the actual word 'friction' only where it seems to help children explain their ideas.

 What situations can you think of where there is friction?
What do you mean by 'friction'?
What effects does friction have in everyday life?
When is friction helpful?
When is friction a nuisance?

Floating and sinking

AREAS FOR INVESTIGATION

◆ Discovering which materials float and which sink.

◆ Feeling and measuring the forces on floating and sinking objects.

◆ Finding ways of making floating things sink, and sinking things float.

KEY IDEAS

◆ Some objects float in water but others sink.

◆ Whether or not something floats depends on a combination of factors, which include the material it is made of, its shape, and the liquid it is in.

◆ *When something floats the forces acting on it are balanced.

◆ *A material will float if its density is less than, or equal to, the density of the liquid it is in.

(*Asterisks indicate ideas which will be developed more fully in later key stages.)

A LOOK AT
floating and sinking

Whether something floats or sinks in water depends on the material it is made of and its shape. Some materials, such as cork, always float. Some materials that normally float may sink if they contain holes and absorb water. Some materials which usually sink can be made to float if they are formed into an object of a particular shape, such as that of a boat.

Floating and sinking can also be explained in terms of the forces involved. An object in water is acted on by the downward pull of gravity, just as it is in air. The water pushes up on the object. If the pull is bigger than the push, the object sinks. If the pull equals the push, the object floats.

Finding out children's ideas

STARTER ACTIVITIES

1 Floating and sinking in the classroom

Ask children to collect a wide variety of ordinary objects to explore:

◆ different materials such as metal, plastic, wood, cork, rock, paper, etc.;
◆ different shapes and sizes such as round and rectangular, large and small objects, hollow and solid, with holes and without.

Use sinks, bowls, buckets or transparent tanks of water. Ask the children to start by dividing the objects into two groups, those they think are 'floaters' and those they think are 'sinkers'.

Then, after giving time for exploration, ask:

 Why do you think some things float in water?
Why do you think some things sink in water?

Children could discuss their ideas or write them down.

For some children this question might be too general. It may be preferable to ask about specific objects:

 Why do you think the coin sinks?

Again, they could give their ideas orally or make an annotated drawing of the water container, showing the floaters and sinkers they have observed and writing a comment against each.

2 Floating and sinking outside

It is also possible to put the above work in an everyday context, for example by following a visit to a river, canal, pond or the seaside with questions to suit the occasion, such as:

  Why do you think the weight on a fishing line sinks while the float floats?
Why do you think a ship floats?
Why does an anchor sink?

Children's ideas

Ideas about floating and sinking

Some children think things float or sink 'because they are meant to'. Objects 'want' to float or 'want' to sink. The following comment comes from a child who seems to believe that whether Plasticine sinks or not depends upon the animal form into which it is made.

> yesterday I made a raddit out of plasticine And I thought it wood sink and it did. Today I made a mouse out of plasticine and I thought it wood float and it did.

Other children give properties of the object as reasons for floating or sinking. Sometimes, however, they focus on properties which do not actually affect whether the object will float or sink. One child, for instance, said that a marble sank because it was blue and big.

Weight is commonly given as one of the factors.

> I think it float's (My boat) because it is Light

I think some objects sink because of the weight, shape and the position it has been put into the water. I think things float because they are light and well ballenced.

Occasionally children realize that weight alone does not explain flotation, but the concept of density is a difficult one. The following statement shows how one child has gone some way towards an understanding of it.

> I think that the wooden block floor because it is quite light for its size

Other children focus on the material, giving it as a reason.

> It won't sink because it is plastic and plastic only floats.
>
> We think the paper floated because it is made from a tree and trees are made from wood and wood floats.

Such generalizations may be partly true, but there are often exceptions. Some kinds of plastic float and some do not; while lignum vitae, an African wood, sinks.

Some children think about floating and sinking in terms of the forces involved.

Some carry the idea of the upward push of water further. A child may believe that floating objects are pushed up by the water and those that sink are pushed down by it. One child had the idea that the way a ship floated depended on how deep the water was and made this comment:

The Container dosen't sink because of force. When pushed down it just Pops up again. Because the water is Forceing the Container upwards. So no matter how hard you push it down, the water will push against the Container, so it stays afloat.

> Underneath a ship there is more water to hold it up. When there is a lot more water there is a lot more pressure coming up to hold the ship up. The water is sort of pushing up.

In this case, the push of the water has been linked to the amount of water under the ship rather than the water the ship has displaced.

Another idea came from a child who had altered a ball of Plasticine to make it float.

The plasticine floats because of the water and gravity. The gravity pushes the plasticine down but the water pushes it up. This means that the water pressure is ~~bigg~~ stronger than the gravity.

In this example, the downward force opposing the upward push of water is called 'gravity'. However, gravity is not seen as the downward pull of the Earth on the Plasticine or the weight of the Plasticine, but rather as something pushing down. Is it the air pushing down? The following was written by a child for whom this was clearly the case.

> If the air pressure is stronger than the water pressure the object would probably sink but if the water pressure is stronger than the air pressure the object would probably float and I don't think it will make any difference about the weight.

It is also noticeable that in both these examples the word 'pressure' has been used instead of 'force'.

Helping children to develop their ideas

The chart on the next page shows how you can help children to develop their ideas from starting points which have given rise to different ideas.

The centre rectangle contains a starter question.

The surrounding 'thought bubbles' contain the sorts of ideas expressed by children.

The further ring of rectangles contains questions posed by teachers in response to the ideas expressed by the children. These questions are meant to prompt children to think about their ideas.

The outer ovals indicate ways in which the children might respond to the teacher's questions.

Some of the shapes have been left blank, as a sign that other ideas may be encountered and other ways of helping children to develop their ideas may be tried.

1 Testing ideas

First encourage children to try out their ideas to see how generally applicable they are. For instance, suppose some children have suggested that an object floats because it is big. The question:

 Do any small things float?

could prompt investigations about size and floating and any links between the two. Some children may suggest that the material an object is made of is important. See the chart for further examples of turning children's ideas into investigations.

 THE MATERIAL FROM WHICH AN OBJECT IS MADE IS A FACTOR WHICH AFFECTS WHETHER IT FLOATS OR SINKS

2 Extending the starter activity

Extend the starter activity along more systematic lines to test other ideas.

For each of a set of objects, such as those given below, ask each child in a group to write down his or her own predictions about whether each object will float or sink, together with reasons. Then they could discuss their ideas with one another. This could lead to reconsideration of initial ideas.

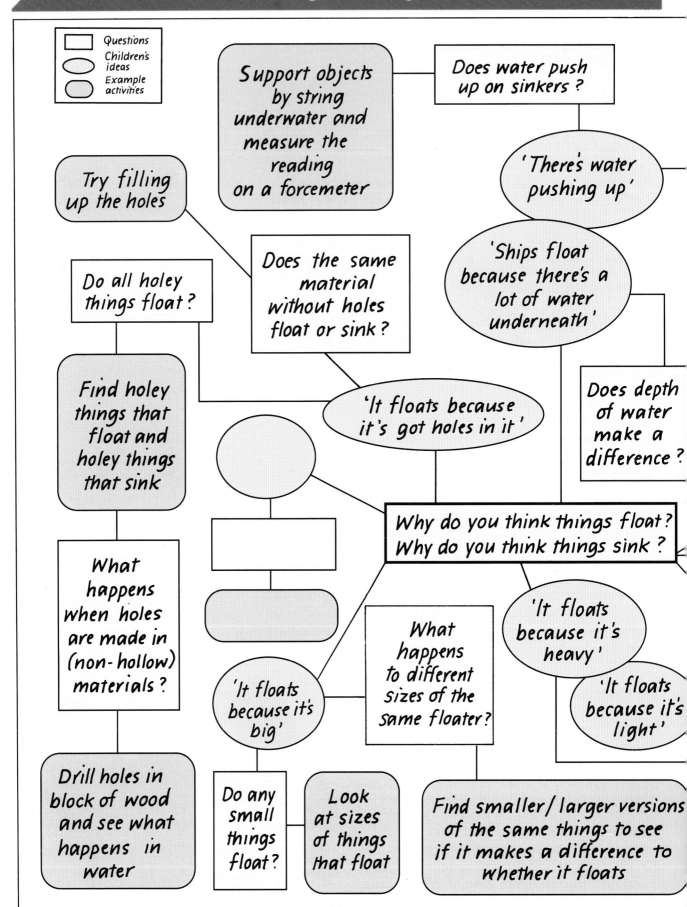

Key:
- Questions (rectangle)
- Children's ideas (oval)
- Example activities (shaded rounded rectangle)

Support objects by string underwater and measure the reading on a forcemeter

Does water push up on sinkers?

Try filling up the holes

'There's water pushing up'

Do all holey things float?

Does the same material without holes float or sink?

'Ships float because there's a lot of water underneath'

Find holey things that float and holey things that sink

'It floats because it's got holes in it'

Does depth of water make a difference?

Why do you think things float? Why do you think things sink?

What happens when holes are made in (non-hollow) materials?

What happens to different sizes of the same floater?

'It floats because it's heavy'

'It floats because it's big'

'It floats because it's light'

Drill holes in block of wood and see what happens in water

Do any small things float?

Look at sizes of things that float

Find smaller/larger versions of the same things to see if it makes a difference to whether it floats

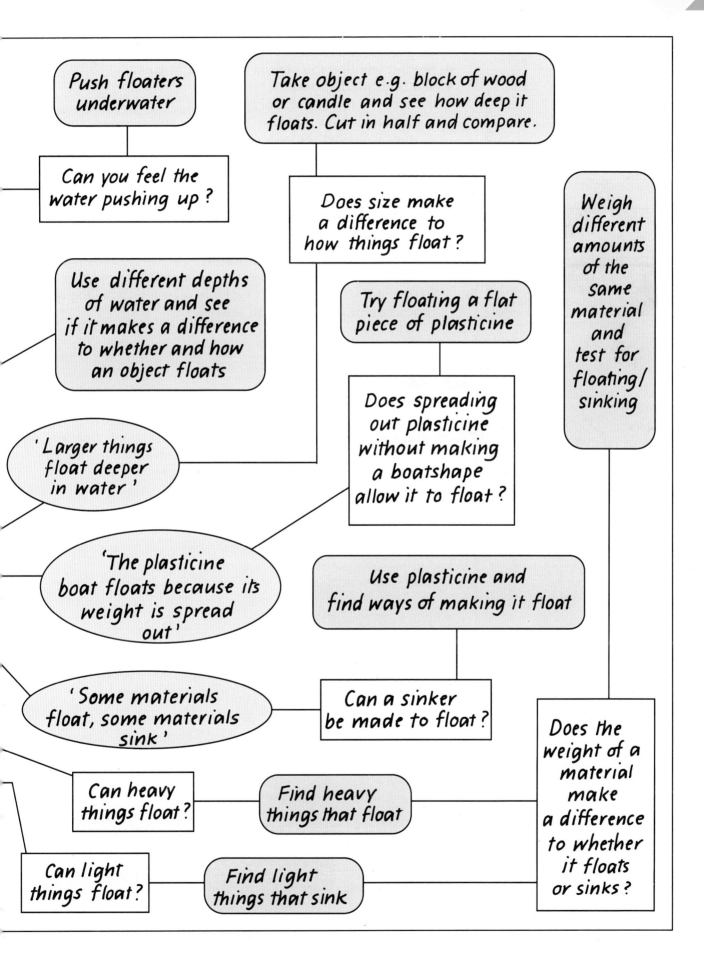

Push floaters underwater

Can you feel the water pushing up?

Take object e.g. block of wood or candle and see how deep it floats. Cut in half and compare.

Does size make a difference to how things float?

Weigh different amounts of the same material and test for floating/sinking

Use different depths of water and see if it makes a difference to whether and how an object floats

Try floating a flat piece of plasticine

Does spreading out plasticine without making a boatshape allow it to float?

'Larger things float deeper in water'

'The plasticine boat floats because its weight is spread out'

Use plasticine and find ways of making it float

'Some materials float, some materials sink'

Can a sinker be made to float?

Does the weight of a material make a difference to whether it floats or sinks?

Can heavy things float?

Find heavy things that float

Can light things float?

Find light things that sink

PREDICTING.
OBSERVING.
INTERPRETING RESULTS
AND FINDINGS.
COMMUNICATING

IF A PREDICTION IS
FOUND TO BE TRUE IT
DOES NOT NECESSARILY
MEAN THAT THE REASON
FOR THE PREDICTION IS
TRUE

The group could be asked to:

◆ collect a range of objects such as nails, paper towels, marbles, margarine tubs, Plasticine, drawing pins, cotton reels, washers, paper clips, pumice stone, sand, plywood, chipboard, plastic cups;
◆ predict whether the objects will float or sink;
◆ test their predictions;
◆ observe the result precisely:
    does it sink quickly?
    does it float at the water surface or within the water?
    does it float one way up but not another?
    how high in the water does it float?
    does it float first, then sink?
◆ record the result in sets, tables, wall charts or drawings;
◆ interpret the results;
◆ discuss ideas about why some objects sink while others float and present these on, say, a poster;
◆ extend the work by looking at liquids which do not mix with water – for example, vegetable oil – following the same procedure of predicting and testing.

3 Everyday instances

Ask children to draw everyday instances of floating. Discuss the examples to reveal what they mean by the word 'floating', and to develop their understanding of it. Introduce further instances such as those shown in the pictures below.

4 Can a sinker be made to float?

This question should encourage further exploration of the factors affecting floating and sinking. Investigations with Plasticine or aluminium foil can help to develop ideas further since these sinkers can be made to float by having their shape altered. Test the effectiveness of the floating vessels by loading them with small objects such as wood blocks or marbles.

Q *Who can make the 'floating vessel' from a 10 cm square piece of aluminium foil which holds the most cargo?*

In this context, the children could consider the Plimsoll line, which is used to show how much cargo ships can safely hold; this is described in *Forces and movement*.

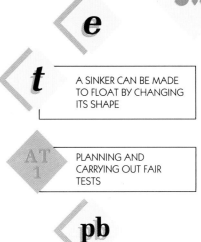

e

t A SINKER CAN BE MADE TO FLOAT BY CHANGING ITS SHAPE

AT 1 — PLANNING AND CARRYING OUT FAIR TESTS

pb

5 Pushes and pulls in floating and sinking

a Trying to sink floating objects

Let children try to sink floating objects by pushing them down. Add objects such as, balls, balloons and plastic containers if these are not already there. Let children compare the push needed to sink different objects.

e

To help children appreciate the upward push of water, ask:

Q *Why do you think you have to push down to sink the plastic container?*
What happens when you release the table tennis ball under water? Why do you think this happens?

t WATER PUSHES UP THINGS THAT FLOAT IN IT

t

THINGS FEEL
LIGHTER IN
WATER BECAUSE
THE WATER IS
PUSHING
THEM UP

e

b Does water also push up against things that sink?

Put this question to children who already have the idea that water pushes up floaters.

This should lead to children supporting objects on string and holding them in air and in water, followed by a discussion of why things feel lighter in water.

c Measuring the upward push of water

AT
1   MEASURING

If children have ideas such as 'the water pushes up more when there's more of it', suggest using a force meter. This allows them to measure forces rather than simply compare pushes by their 'feel'.

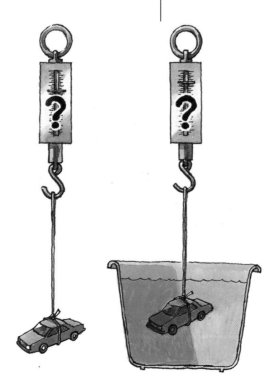

To show the overall force on a floating object, attach a floater by string to a force meter and slowly lower it into the water until the point when the string is about to slacken.

Q *Why do you think the reading becomes zero?*

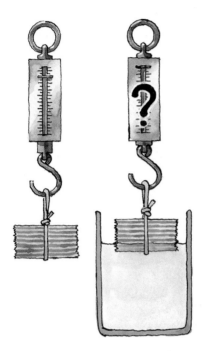

t WHEN AN OBJECT FLOATS THE FORCES ON IT ARE IN BALANCE

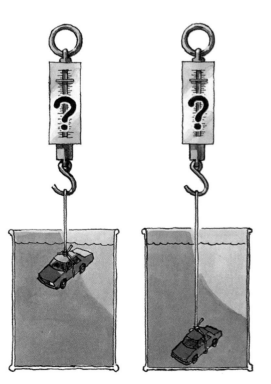

t WATER PUSHES UP AGAINST A 'SINKER' IMMERSED IN WATER. THE UPWARD PUSH OF WATER ON AN IMMERSED OBJECT DOES NOT DEPEND ON THE AMOUNT OR DEPTH OF WATER

Structures and balance

AREAS FOR INVESTIGATION

◆ Examination of a variety of structures.

◆ Characteristics of strong/stable structures.

◆ Balancing objects in different ways.

Much of the work in this theme at Key Stage 2 is to provide a wide range of experiences from which work at Key Stage 3 can be developed.

KEY IDEAS

◆ All things are pulled towards the centre of the Earth; it is a force called gravity which makes them fall.

◆ Forces can change the shape of objects.

◆ *Stable/balanced objects are being acted on by balanced forces.

◆ *An object is most stable when its centre of mass is as low as possible.

(*Asterisks indicate ideas which will be developed more fully in later key stages.)

A LOOK AT
structures and balance

Pushing, pulling, twisting and squeezing can change the shape of things. The amount of change depends on the amount of force used and which material it is applied to.

Materials differ in the ease with which their shape can be changed. Some, such as rubber, alter relatively easily while others, such as steel, require a much greater force to produce a comparable change. Their pliability is also affected by the shape of the piece of material. A thin metal wire twists more easily than a metal block of the same weight.

The strength of a structure depends not only on the material from which it is made and the form of that material, but also how the parts are arranged. Some arrangements, such as the triangular patterns often seen in girders, give stronger structures than others. The strength of a structure can be tested by applying an increasing force to it until it breaks.

Bricks in a straight upright column are in balance, but if the topmost bricks are pushed too far out of line with the others their own weight (the pull of the Earth on them) will cause them to topple over and fall. Similarly, a solid column will fall down if its centre of mass is too far to one side so that it is not above the area of its base.

Even something that is in balance can be tipped over by pushing it sideways – especially if it is light, or tall and thin.

Things will not overbalance so easily if they are weighted at the bottom. (Naturally this does not apply to a column of loose bricks.) A wider base also makes it harder to topple something over.

In balancing objects the forces involved are operating equally about the point of balance. Balancing toys are made so that a push to one side is counterbalanced by a force which returns the toy to its original position.

Finding out children's ideas

STARTER ACTIVITIES

It is important to get children thinking about why particular structures stay up while others are more likely to fall down. Starter activities should be designed to provide a stimulus followed by some thinking time before the children are questioned about their ideas. All the activities given as examples below take this into consideration.

1 Building block towers

Ask children to:

◆ build a tower from a single column of 'bricks' as high as they can;
◆ use the same number of bricks to make a stronger tower;
◆ draw a picture of their highest and strongest tower.

 Which do you think is the best tower?
What do you think makes your tower fall over?
What makes the best tower the best?
How could you make your tower better?
What do you think is the most important thing for a tower to do?
Why does a tower sometimes fall down on its own?
What do you think holds the tower up?

2 Visits to buildings, bridges or a building site

Visits provide a stimulus for further activities and give children an excellent opportunity to discuss and explain their ideas on the way structures are built and what helps them stay up.

> **!** CHILDREN SHOULD BE MADE AWARE OF THE DANGERS OF BUILDING SITES; CHECK SCHOOL POLICY ON VISITS

3 Balancing objects

Display a range of objects which balance in different ways, including, for instance, a 'see-saw balance', scales and balancing 'executive toys'.

Q *What do you think makes these balance?*
Why do you think these don't fall over?

Encourage children to record their ideas in some way, possibly in a class log book. Discuss these with them in order to explore the ideas and express them more precisely.

4 Twists and squeezes

The materials used to make structures are selected for properties which include, for example, the ability to retain their shape under stress.

Find out children's ideas about the effects of twisting and squeezing on different materials. Provide a range of materials such as wire, Plasticine, plastic strip and foam, rubber, and metal strip with an invitation to try and change their shape.

Q *How did you change the shape of this?*
What happened?
Why do you think this happened?
Could you change it in any other way?
Do you think you could stop the change happening?
How would you do it?

Children's ideas

Many children may not have thought about how structures stay together and maintain their shape. However, from a very early age most children build towers from blocks and then knock them down, or find that the tower reaches a point at which it collapses. So they will already have some experience of the effects of forces on structures. Ideas related to a particular kind of structure are given here, but other structures may be used if this seems appropriate.

During the research for this teachers' guide, when children were asked to build a strong tower from a given number of bricks they produced three principal designs:

◆ a single column of bricks supported on a wide base;
◆ parallel columns of bricks;
◆ interlocking bricks.

Tower of cubes

I like the stand of it with just one line of cubes it falls over esily butthenew one I made does'nt fall over esily because it has two lines of cubes I have put them strait.

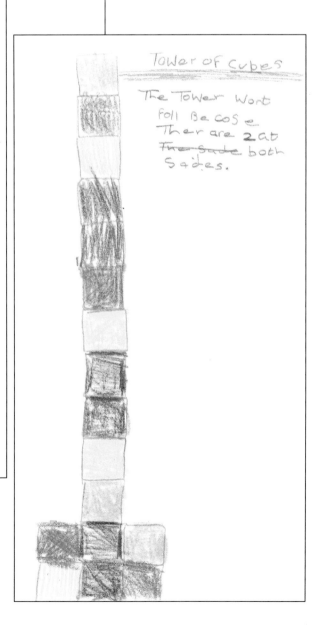

Tower of cubes

The Tower wont foll Becose ther are 2 at both sades.

This activity reflects the complex way in which children's ideas develop. Children design towers which have relatively low centres of mass and which will not rock easily from side to side. However, their explanations of why the design is better do not yet refer to the ideas of stability and balance. Similarly, references to gravity and weight causing the towers to fall over tend to be made by older children.

It was usually the older children who identified a relationship between the width of the base and the increased stability.

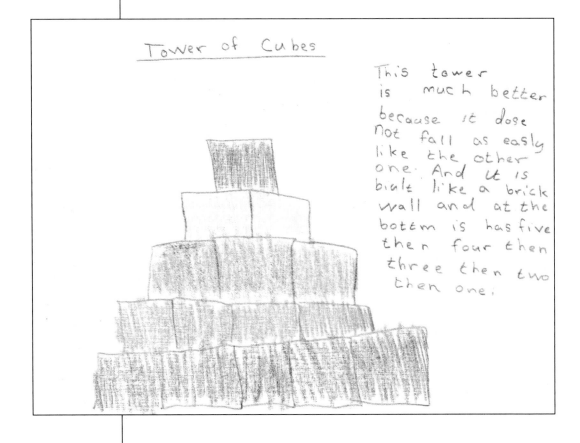

Tower of Cubes

This tower is much better because it dose not fall as easly like the other one. And it is bialt like a brick wall and at the botem is has five then four then three then two then one.

The following three examples all show a structure with a wide base supporting the column, but none of the explanations refers to the base directly supporting the column.

The bricks at each side of the tower make it balance.

(These drawings have been annotated by the teacher to show what the children said about them.)

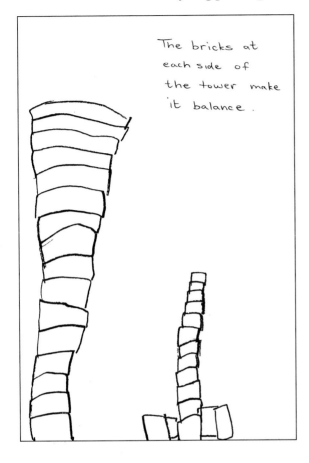

Tower of cubes

This will not fall over because the blocks are together on both side of the tall pile.

I think my tower stands up better because they are straight.

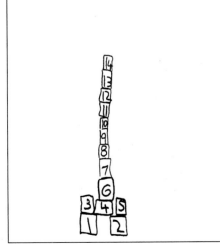

Some children expressed the idea that interlocking bricks in the structure played a part in the stability of the tower.

The following response suggests that children think that one column can prop up the other to stop it falling. Thus neighbouring columns, even when imperfectly aligned, are regarded as counteracting each other's instability.

It didn't fall because its built up in threes.
The threes touch each other and stay up.

The degree to which interlocking bricks were used varied from a single row to complete towers of interlocking bricks, as in the following examples.

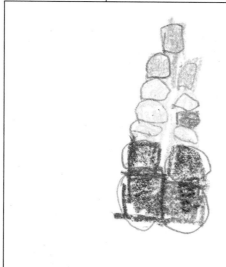

The one on the top keeps the tower from falling over.

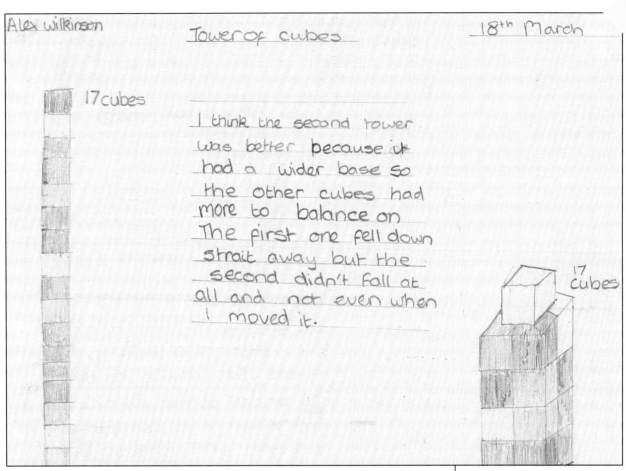

Alex wilkinson — Tower of cubes — 18th March

17 cubes

I think the second tower was better because it had a wider base so the other cubes had more to balance on. The first one fell down strait away but the second didn't fall at all and not even when I moved it.

17 cubes

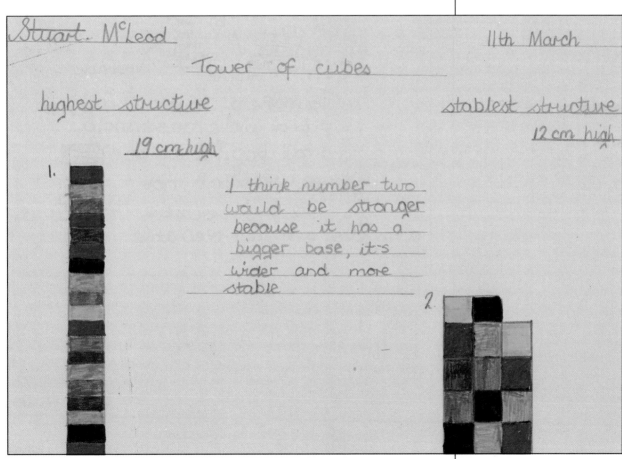

Stuart. McLeod — 11th March

Tower of cubes

highest structure

19 cm high

1.

stablest structure

12 cm high

I think number two would be stronger because it has a bigger base, it's wider and more stable

2.

The final example identifies gravity as a force involved in causing a tower to fall.

Why a tall tower
falls
Gravity pull

equal weight   unequal weight   gravity pull   gravity

When a tower is straight,
the gravity is much more stable
But when it is wobbly, it
is easy for Gravity to pull
the bricks to the floor/table.
and when the weight is
on one side, the tower
will fall.
a)   b)
          ✓   ✗
     stable   unstable

To make a tower stronger,
put a wide base and a
small top. The walls   a)
are built like B, not
like a) because   b)
a walls are fall-over-able.

Helping children to develop their ideas

The chart on the next page shows how you can help children to develop their ideas from starting points which have given rise to different ideas.

The centre rectangle contains a starter question.

The surrounding 'thought bubbles' contain the sorts of ideas expressed by children.

The further ring of rectangles contains questions posed by teachers in response to the ideas expressed by the children. These questions are meant to prompt children to think about their ideas.

The outer ovals indicate ways in which the children might respond to the teacher's questions.

Some of the shapes have been left blank, as a sign that other ideas may be encountered and other ways of helping children to develop their ideas may be tried.

AT 1   OBSERVING

1 Looking at different structures

Children should look at buildings such as churches, houses, and tower blocks, and also at bridges. Plan a visit during which features of structures can be identified. These might include:

- archways with keystones;
- buttresses of different types;
- restraining bars on bridges and open towers;
- lintels over doors and windows;
- foundations;
- the arrangement of bricks.

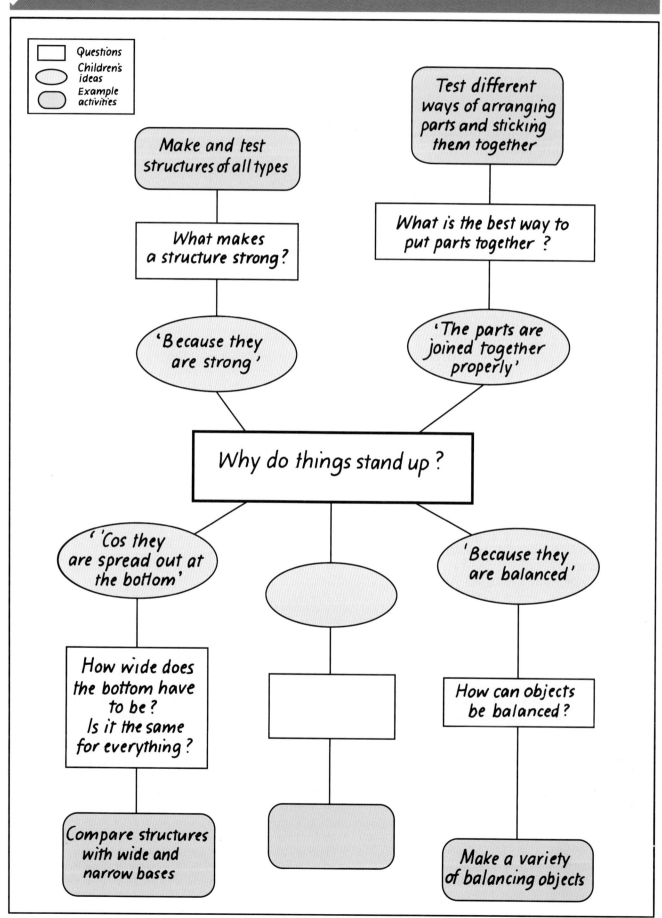

Questions

Children's ideas

Example activities

Make and test structures of all types

Test different ways of arranging parts and sticking them together

What makes a structure strong?

What is the best way to put parts together?

'Because they are strong'

'The parts are joined together properly'

Why do things stand up?

''Cos they are spread out at the bottom'

'Because they are balanced'

How wide does the bottom have to be? Is it the same for everything?

How can objects be balanced?

Compare structures with wide and narrow bases

Make a variety of balancing objects

Discuss the features and the role they play in the overall structure.

2 Building structures

Try to model structures seen elsewhere, using this as an opportunity for children to devise investigations to test the structures in an appropriate manner. This will involve the children in:

◆ designing fair tests;
◆ making predictions;
◆ asking questions;
◆ making measurements of different variables such as force, height and mass;
◆ drawing conclusions.

Present these activities as problem-solving exercises by setting limits to the size of the model, the materials to be used, etc. Alternatively, ask children to make a structure which has, for example, the best stability, in order to focus their attention on particular aspects of the concepts involved.

Children may find the pictures of bridges in *More about forces and movement* helpful.

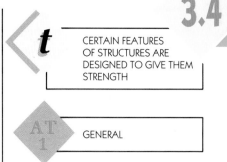

t CERTAIN FEATURES OF STRUCTURES ARE DESIGNED TO GIVE THEM STRENGTH

3.4

AT 1 GENERAL

pb

AT 1 — MEASURING

a Building block towers as an extension of the starter activity

Using blocks of the same size can be limiting, so introduce blocks of different shapes and sizes to help children explore a variety of designs. A swinging ball is a simple device for testing these structures.

Record the strength of the tower in terms of the angle of release of the ball or the number of swings needed to knock it down.

Introduce other construction toys, including Lego, to extend the range of possible structures.

b Building bridges

Bridges come in many different shapes and sizes and provide excellent opportunities for exploring the effects of forces on and in structures. This activity might start with a survey of different types of bridge, and then be developed by the children designing, building and testing their own in a range of materials. For example, paper or thin card can be used to find:

 Which is the best girder?

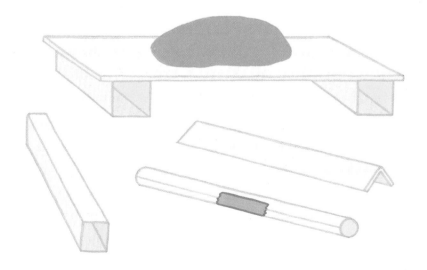

AT 1 — PLANNING AND CARRYING OUT FAIR TESTS

More complex designs can be undertaken, using 'girders' made from tightly rolled-up newspaper and joined with sticky tape.

You could discuss with the children the pictures of different kinds of bridge in *More about forces and movement*.

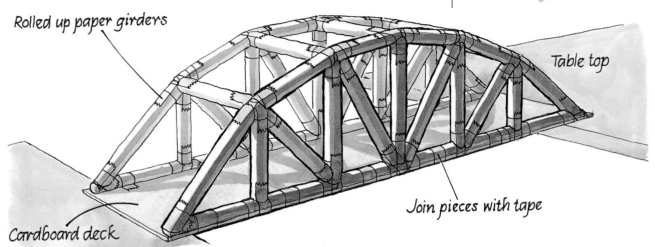

Rolled up paper girders

Table top

Join pieces with tape

Cardboard deck

3 Balancing objects

These rely on the fact that the forces involved are operating equally about the point of balance.

Explore these through a see-saw type balance or a see-saw in the park. Children can find out which objects balance. Ask:

Q *Where is the pivot point on the object?*

Ask the children to try and identify patterns in the results. If you have a mathematical see-saw type balance, some children may be able to look at the problem in a quantitative manner.

AT 1 — INTERPRETING RESULTS AND FINDINGS

Q *Can you find a pattern which helps you to balance the see-saw?*

t — BALANCED OBJECTS HAVE BALANCED FORCES

Examine why and when an object topples over. Link this to the building of towers and other appropriate topics, such as the effect of wind on high-sided vehicles and on sailing boats when they capsize.

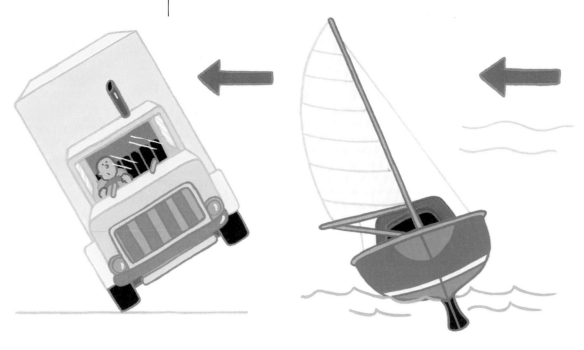

In a similar way, a container for pencils or rulers might often topple over. This happens particularly if the container is narrow, short or light. Set the children this challenge:

Q *How can you prevent the container from falling over so often?*
Can you find a better kind of container? What makes it better?

The experience of balancing toys given in the starter activity can also be extended. Ask children to design their own balancing toys. They might, for example, make a cardboard clown and balance it on a piece of string.

t THINGS WILL NOT OVERBALANCE SO EASILY IF THEY ARE WEIGHTED AT THE BOTTOM OR IF THEY HAVE A WIDER BASE

Q *How can you make the clown balance better?*
What is it about the design of the clown that makes it balance better?

The pictures in *Forces and movement* give examples of things which balance and things which don't. You could encourage the children to discuss these among themselves.

4 Twists and squeezes

Twisting and squeezing changes the shape of objects. This provides a natural link with work on materials. The starter activity can easily be extended by systematically testing different materials (to destruction if necessary) by applying twists, squeezes, pulls and pushes of various strengths. This gives opportunities for close observation and devising fair tests. More details of these activities are in the *Materials* teachers' guide.

3.4

t ADDING WEIGHTS SUCH AS PAPER CLIPS TO THE FEET SHOULD MAKE THE CLOWN BALANCE BETTER

pb

AT 1 INTERPRETING RESULTS AND FINDINGS

CHAPTER 4 Assessment

4.1 Introduction

You will have been assessing your children's ideas and skills by using the activities in this teachers' guide. This on-going, formative assessment is essentially part of teaching since what you find is immediately used in suggesting the next steps to help the children's progress. But this information can also be brought together and summarized for purposes of recording and reporting progress. This summary of performance has to be in terms of National Curriculum level descriptions at the end of the key stages, and some schools keep records in terms of levels at other times.

This chapter helps you summarize the information you have from children's work in terms of level descriptions. Examples of work relating to the theme of this guide are discussed and features which indicate activity at a certain level are pointed out to show what to look for in your pupils' work as evidence of achievement at one level or another. It is necessary, however, to look across the full range of work, and not judge from any single event or piece of work.

There are two sets of examples provided. The first is the assessment of skills in the context of the activities related to the concepts covered in this guide. The second deals with the development of these concepts.

4.2 Assessment of skills (AT1)

Things to look for when pupils are investigating forces and movement, as indicating progress from level 2 to level 5

Level 2: Making suggestions as well as responding to others' suggestions about how to find things out about or compare movement and forces. Using equipment, such as toys or models which move or objects for floating and sinking, to make observations. Recording what they find and comparing it with what they expected.

Level 3: Saying what they expect to happen when something is changed and suggesting ways of collecting information to test their predictions. Carrying out fair tests, knowing why they are fair, and making measurements. Recording what they find in a variety of ways; noticing any patterns in it.

Level 4: Making predictions which guide the planning of fair tests. Using suitable equipment and making adequate and relevant observations. Using tables and charts to record measurements and other observations. Interpreting, drawing conclusions and attempting to relate findings to scientific knowledge.

Level 5: Planning controlled investigations of predictions which are based on scientific knowledge. Using equipment carefully, repeating observations as necessary. Using line graphs to record and help interpretation; considering findings in relation to scientific knowledge.

Within a topic of transport a teacher discussed the movement of toy cars in order to consider the effects of forces on movement. Children had a sloping surface whose inclination could be changed and various surfaces on which the cars moved on reaching the base of the slope. Groups of children considered the effects of different surfaces such as coconut matting, a piece of carpet and polythene. Some investigated the effect of water, oil or polish on the car's movement. Other children investigated what happened when the angle of the slope was altered. Using blocks they altered the height of the slope and measured the distance the car travelled or the time taken to travel a particular distance. Fair testing was encouraged through questioning.

> *How will you start the car moving?*
> *At what point on the slope will you start the car?*

The children were encouraged to share their investigations with each other during a group reporting session. The issue of fair testing was again addressed as children presented their interpretations of their results. The discussion also focused on the children's interpretation of their results. They were encouraged to consider whether their interpretations of the evidence were different.

Stephanie investigated the effect of changing the slope. Her account is somewhat contradictory but it seems that she is comparing the car on a slope with the car on flat ground. Her record includes no measurements but her conclusion is based on a series of observations relevant to what she wanted to find out. This is evidence of work at level 2.

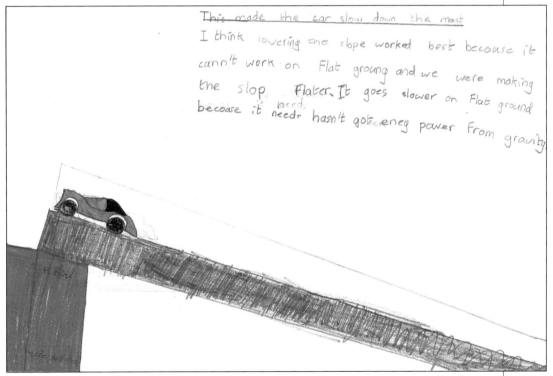

Stephanie

①

coconut mat

The car will roll down the slope but stop when it gets to the mat because of the bristles. The bristle gets in the way.

②

carpet

The car will roll until it gets to the carpet. On the carpet it will slow because the carpet is rather fluffy.

③

sheet of polythene

The car will carry on rolling on the polythene because it is spot smooth. Cars go faster at the bottom of the slope because they pick up speed

④

polished floor

On the polished floor the car will carry keep on rolling because it is (the floor) hard and shiny. I think it will carry ongoing for the longest on a polished floor

Angela

I think that the car will slow down when it reaches the mat because it is spikey.

I think the car rolls down the slope because it has wheels and gravity pulls it.

COCONUT MAT

Sarah

Angela recorded her predictions about how the car would behave on different surfaces. Her drawings show how her predictions could be tested. The position of the car in each drawing may not indicate awareness of the need to test fairly, although the teacher noted that when she carried out the tests she did place the car at the top of the slope in each case and she may have realized that this was necessary when carrying out the investigation in practice. If discussion confirmed that she knew the tests should be fair this would complete the picture of work at level 3.

In her writing, Sarah adds her ideas about why the car rolls down in terms of gravity. As far as her ideas are concerned her work suggests level 4 but her investigation skills are, like Sarah's, approaching level 3.

Gerard's group

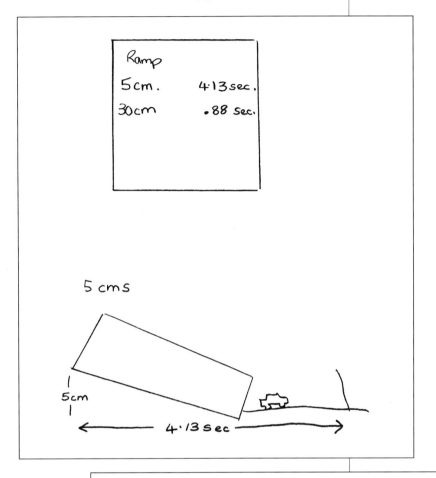

Gerard's group continued

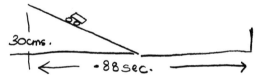

If the ramp is less than 5 cm the car does not go down.
As they keep lifting the ramp the car goes further and faster.

Why?
the height of the ramp
How slanted it is

Can things move without being pushed or pulled. Yes (James) We can
What moves your car onthe ramp →
Gravity (Gerard).

Gravity is something that pulls things down unless they are stuck up there. (James)

It might be gravity that is pulling the car down

dont think so.   think so.

Donna Pool   Joanne.
                              Gerard.
                              James.
                              Steven

Gerard and his friends investigated the effect of altering the height of the ramp on the time the car took to travel a particular distance. Their teacher's observations of their work indicated that they recognized the need for measurement and carried it out carefully. In discussion with the teacher they provided an account of what they noticed, indicating that they had noticed patterns in the height of the ramp and the speed of the car.

Gerard's group continued

The children's explanation of their results was further probed by the teacher, whose notes reveal that they attempted to use the idea of gravity in their interpretation but were tentative about this. Not all the pupils thought that 'it might be gravity pulling the car down' and seemed open to alternative suggestions. By encouraging these kinds of discussions the teacher was providing the children with opportunities to consider their findings in terms of scientific knowledge and thus helping them make progress to more secure working at level 4.

4.3 Assessment of children's understanding (part of AT 4)

Aspects of work relating to forces and movement indicating progress from level 2 to level 5:

Level 2: Describing and comparing the movement of objects in terms of speed and direction. Describing how forces change the movement of objects.

Level 3: Recognizing that forces can change the shape of an object, as in squashing or compressing a spring, or change the direction or speed of its movement.

Level 4: Realizing that forces act in certain directions and that more than one force can act on an object and can act in different directions. Recognizing gravity, magnetic attraction, friction and air resistance, as forces which cause change in movement.

Level 5: Recognizing that change in shape and movement are caused by unbalanced forces acting on an object and that no change in motion occurs when forces acting are balanced, as when an object is at rest on a surface or floating in water.

When the car rolls down the slope gravity pulls on it so it is possible for the toy car to roll down the slope. it goes faster nearer the bottom of the hill than the top because gravity has been pulling for a longer time so it can go faster it stops after a while after the slope because all the power it had it cannot stop straig away and friction help it to stop as well because friction tries to stop movement.

Jane

Jane

When the ball or aeroplane goes in the air the push of your arm makes it go up gradually and then when it gets weaker gravity starts pulling down so the ball comes down gradually

gravity starts pulling here

the push from your arm gets weaker here

In her explanation of the car moving down the slope, Jane mentions that gravity is pulling the car down the slope and that the effect of gravity is to make the car go faster as it reaches the bottom. She mentions friction as stopping the movement, although she does not identify it as a force. Her description of the movement of a ball thrown into the air shows knowledge that forces acting stop it continuing upwards. But she explains that gravity 'starts pulling' at a certain point, which reflects a common belief that gravity only operates when things move down and not all the time. Jane's work shows recognition of how forces change the direction and speed of the movement of object and is at level 3.

In the description, on page 36, of the flight of her paper aeroplane, Adele mentions two effects of forces: in changing the direction of the flight and in the nose of the aeroplane getting 'a bit bashed'. She does not explicitly identify these effects as being due to forces and it would be necessary to ask her to explain her ideas of the causes before deciding whether her work has reached level 3.

Linda

When you throw a ball through the air your mucsdes transmit energy to your hand which, in turn throws the ball. Gravity is pulling on the ball as it goes up, because if it wasn't the ball would just got up and never come down. So when the push from the muscles wears off, gravity pulls it down.

In the same earlier chapter, on page 37, the child's work indicates a grasp of opposing forces, although, again, the word force is not used. The drawing and the annotation show that the child visualizes the forces as acting in certain directions and, by implication, opposing each other and so explaining why the paper aeroplane comes down. The child has left out of account the force caused by air resistance, but in other respects the work is at level 4.

In contrast with Jane, Linda's explanation of the ball's movement indicates that there is an initial force which starts the object moving and that gravity acts to pull the ball down all the time. Her idea that, as the ball is going upwards, 'the push' wears off and gravity out balances it, suggests that she is working towards a notion of unbalanced forces and is making progress towards level 5.

Simon explains how forces explain why the container does not sink. He recognizes opposing forces acting and keeping the object afloat. It would be necessary to probe his understanding of the forces acting when the container is floating and not being pushed down to decide whether his work has reached level 5.

The container dosen't sink because of force. When Sir poshed it down it just Pops up again. Becouse the water is forceing the container opwards, So no matter how hard you push it down, the water will posh against the container, So it stays afloat.

Simon

CHAPTER 5

Background science

What are forces?

Force and movement

The word 'force' has several common everyday meanings. It makes us think of being made to do things. As such it implies coercion and compulsion; for example, 'John was forced by the bad weather to stay at home.' Force may also be associated with strength and power, as in 'the armed forces'.

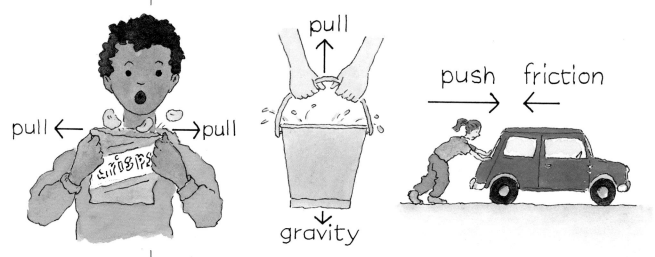

Examples of everyday forces

In science the word 'force' conveys a different, though related, meaning. Scientists use it in the sense of forces that can push, pull, twist or squeeze; most importantly, they realize that forces of this kind are acting on objects everywhere.

The pushes, pulls, twists and squeezes can:

Some effects of forces

◆ make stationary objects move;
◆ make moving objects speed up;
◆ make moving objects slow down;
◆ make moving objects stop;
◆ make moving objects change direction;
◆ change the shape of objects.

Thus forces can cause changes in movement or in shape. Whenever any change takes place to the speed, direction of movement or shape of an object it is because a force is acting on it.

This means that if something is moving at a steady speed in a straight line, all the forces acting on it must be in balance so that they cancel each other out. If they did not balance, the object would change its speed or direction. Saying that the forces cancel each other does not mean that there are no forces present. A boat moving straight forward at a steady speed is driven forwards by its propeller. This is clearly a forward push. But the push must be equal to and balanced by the forces which are resisting the movement of the boat, which in this case are the resistance (that is, friction) of the water and the air through which the boat is being pushed. If these forces did not together exactly balance the forward push, the boat's speed would not be constant. Equally, the downward pull of gravity on the boat (weight) must be balanced by the upthrust of the water buoying it up; or it would be sinking or rising in the water (see 'Floating and sinking', on page 109).

Forces acting on a moving boat

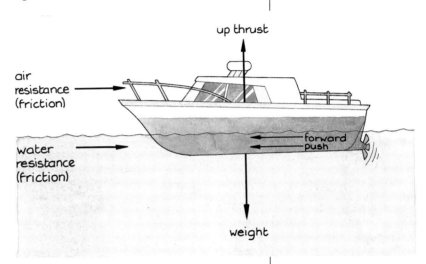

Slowing down, staying put and friction

A penny slid across a table slows down and comes to rest. Slowing down is such a natural event that it is easy to assume that it takes place without any forces being involved. The penny comes to a halt, however, because there is a force acting on it. That force is called **friction**. On Earth, whenever two surfaces move relative to one another – even when an object moves through the air – there is always friction.

In a frictionless environment, a moving object would continue to move at the same speed in the same direction for ever (unless some other force acted on it to change its movement). Almost complete absence of friction is attained in space travel. In space there is practically no material for a rocket to move through. So once set in motion, the object keeps moving.

Some devices, such as brakes, use friction to work. The brakes of a bicycle are lever mechanisms which press a pair of rubber blocks with considerable force, so as to get a large amount of friction, against the rims of the wheels. Our own grip on the Earth is considerably reduced when moving on surfaces where friction is less: a polished floor, an icy pavement, a banana skin. These examples indicate how friction is affected by the nature of the surfaces in contact. Rougher surfaces give more grip, so car tyres have to be replaced when their tread gets worn off. People are less likely to slip when wearing mountain boots with chunky soles than smooth leather soled shoes. Without friction we would be unable to walk. In walking, we push backwards on the

ground. Friction causes the ground to exert a force in the opposite direction, so our feet stay in place and the force moves our body forwards.

It is sometimes thought that friction cannot occur if there is no movement between surfaces. This is not so. Consider, for example, a box stationary on a slope. Gravity pulls it downwards, and without friction the box would slide down the slope. But frictional force between the box and the slope stops it from sliding.

Forces acting when we walk

These examples involve only friction between two solid surfaces. Friction does not only occur between solids; it also exists between a moving solid and a liquid – for instance, between a boat and the water it is moving through. A gas can also cause friction, as you will appreciate when pedalling a bicycle into the wind. This kind of friction is called air resistance. To keep going at a steady speed, a cyclist must apply a force which is equal to the force of air resistance and friction on the bicycle.

Falling

Falling, weight and gravity

From a very early age children start to learn how the world works. From countless games in the high chair, they discover that when you push a spoon over the edge it falls (and that someone picks it up again!). They soon get the idea that falling is a natural process and that the only thing that stops things falling is some kind of support. It is not surprising that children often fail to realize that it is a force that causes objects to fall. This is the force called **gravity**.

All objects attract one another. The force of attraction that they exert depends on their mass. Between small objects the force of attraction is so small as to be negligible. The Earth has an enormous mass and so the force of attraction between it and other objects is noticeable. The weight of an object is a measure of how much the Earth pulls on it

Forces can be measured with a spring balance. The more the spring is pulled, the further it stretches. The amount of pull is measured in newtons. Since weight is the force exerted by gravity on an object, weights are measured scientifically in newtons. 1 newton (1 N) is approximately equal to the force of Earth's gravity acting on 100 grams of matter. Everyday spring balances are usually calibrated in grams or other units of mass, though they do not really measure mass. A beam balance, where an object is balanced by things of known mass (confusingly called 'weights'), does measure mass.

More about gravity

People can push and pull things. They can also be pushed and pulled themselves. Yet even though gravity is pulling on them, they are so used to this that they are not aware of it in the same way as other forces. There are therefore several common ideas about gravity which are not scientifically correct. Several of these beliefs are about gravity and space. For instance, pictures of space capsules apparently floating in space have given many people the idea that gravity is present only if air is also present, and that it does not operate above the atmosphere. In fact no substance is needed for gravity to act and it is thus still present in space. Astronauts orbiting the Earth 'experience' the sensation of weightlessness, but gravity is still acting on them, keeping them in orbit around the Earth. Without gravity they would move off along a straight line and be lost for ever.

In contrast, gravity is sometimes believed to increase with height above the Earth – this is because an object hits the ground at a greater speed if it is dropped from a greater height. In fact the gravitational attraction of an object depends on how near it is to the Earth. Thus gravity actually decreases with height above the Earth, although the difference is negligible when comparing two objects falling from relatively low though differing heights. The reason for the object falling from a greater height hitting the ground at a greater speed is that gravity makes things accelerate at a steady rate, and the higher object has had a greater distance over which to accelerate, something you would appreciate if you jumped off a bridge.

Some further points can be made about gravity. It is not a push holding things up nor a push holding things down. It is not affected by the substance between objects and so is not reduced in liquids. It is not caused by the Earth spinning – it would still exist if the Earth stopped turning. The Moon's pull on objects is less than the Earth's but gravity still exists there. In fact the pull of the Moon on Earth's oceans causes the tides. Gravitation is the force responsible for the orbits of planets. The Earth goes round the Sun as a result of the Sun's gravitational attraction on the Earth; satellites orbit the Earth because of the gravitational pull of the Earth on them.

The direction in which the Earth's gravity acts is towards its centre. This means that there is no absolute direction called 'down'. A drawing to show rain falling at different places around the Earth would therefore look like this.

Rain falling at several places on the Earth

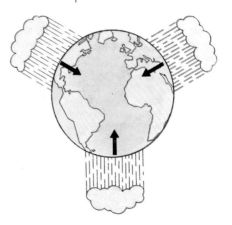

Falling again

Some scientific ideas about force are contrary to expectation. It took the revolutionary genius of the minds of Galileo and Newton to overturn what appeared to be obvious.

Consider, for example, two objects, say a penny and a brick, released from the same height above the ground. Children (and many adults) are likely to believe that the brick will fall more quickly and reach the ground first, because it is heavier. But what actually happens? Both objects fall at the same rate and reach the ground at the same time. This does not happen if the objects differ in shape considerably, such as a coin and a feather – the feather is slowed more by air resistance, which depends on the surface area of an object. For objects with comparable ratios of air resistance to mass, the rate of fall is almost the same. Yet even if you demonstrate this to some people, their belief may be so strong that they 'see' the heavier object hit the ground first. Observations may be heavily influenced by expectations about what will happen.

Dropping two objects of different masses

Rolling down a slope

What makes a ball roll down a slope? How is this connected with the same ball falling? In both cases it is the gravitational pull of the Earth on the ball, its weight, that makes it move. A slope is a very simple machine, which diverts part of the force sideways. It may be difficult for children to generalize so that they can see the similarity between falling down and rolling at an angle.

An object rolling down a slope

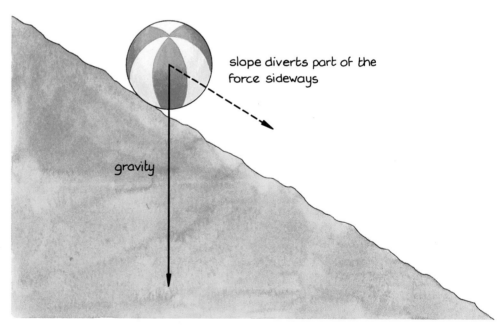

slope diverts part of the force sideways

gravity

As in the case of falling objects, a heavier and lighter object released from the same point on the ramp should reach the bottom at the same time. In practice this is often demonstrated with toy cars, and does not work because they experience different amounts of friction from their wheels and axles. Two coins of different sizes give a satisfactory result.

The extent to which the slope diverts gravity sideways depends on its angle, so that objects take longer to roll down a shallower slope.

Throwing things upwards

Think about throwing a ball vertically upwards. What force is acting on the ball as it goes up? It is tempting to think that the force of the throw remains in the ball as it goes up. In the words of one child:

> *Gravity is pulling on the ball as it goes up, because if it wasn't, the ball would just go up and never come down. So when the push from the muscles wears off, gravity pulls it down.*

For this child, gravity appears to be in opposition to a force in the ball which diminishes as the ball slows down on its journey upwards. Historically such a force was called impetus. This idea is wrong, though.

The scientific explanation of this event is that an upward force is exerted on the ball only while your hand is actually pushing on it. The only force acting on the ball after leaving the hand (neglecting air resistance) is the downwards pull of gravity, whether that ball is rising or falling. That force slows the ball down on its upward flight until it comes to rest at the topmost point it reaches. The same force causes the ball to speed up again as it falls.

Throwing a ball in the air

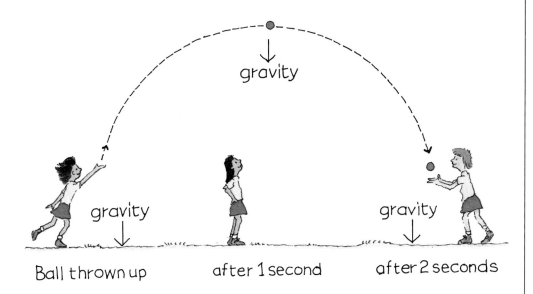

gravity

gravity   gravity

Ball thrown up   after 1 second   after 2 seconds

Two important points about forces can be noted from this example.

1 When a force causes a change in an object's movement (or shape), that force is acting on the object rather than being within it.

2 An object is not necessarily moving in the direction of a force acting on it. Another example is a car when the brakes are applied. The frictional force provided by the brakes is acting in the opposite direction to the movement of the car.

Structures and balance

Recognizing when forces are present

A child can move a toy car by pushing it. She might also be moved by another child pushing her in the playground. These are examples of forces which children can directly feel. Consequently, some children associate pushes and pulls only with human actions and reactions. However, gravitational, magnetic and frictional forces are all examples of forces which act independent of any human agent.

Balanced forces

Balanced forces on a moving and a stationary object

Sometimes things are subjected to a number of forces which exactly cancel each other out. In effect, the overall force is zero. This situation can occur for a moving thing or for one which is stationary. In the former case, the effect of the balanced forces is for the object to continue moving in the same direction at the same velocity. The latter case is precisely the same, the velocity here being nil.

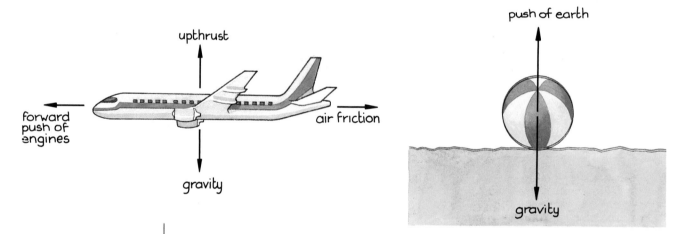

Children are likely to believe that if something is not moving there are no forces acting on it. Consider the example of a book resting on a table. The book's weight is a downward pull on it by the Earth. The other force on the book is from the table pushing up on it. The downward pull and the upward push are equal and opposite and so the book remains stationary.

Perhaps children can more easily appreciate the situation in which they themselves are sitting in a chair. Their weight is a downward pull on them counterbalanced by the upwards push of the chair on them, which they can actually feel. (If the downward pull is greater than the upward push the chair will collapse!)

Many situations are considerably more complex than this. Bridges and buildings contain structural elements which distribute forces, so that there are forces acting in various directions. As long as these forces are all balanced by the structure, and it is strong enough to withstand them, the bridge or building stays up.

Seesaws

Seesaws can also be made to balance. The situation is not a simple balancing of forces, however, because the forces act at different distances from the pivot.

Children soon find out that a light child can balance a heavy one by sitting further away from the pivot than the heavier one. On the seesaw each child is providing a turning force around the pivot. The turning effect of the force depends on both the size of the force and its distance from the pivot. When the force multiplied by the distance from the pivot is the same for each side of the seesaw, it will balance. Thus a 15 kg child 2 metres from the pivot will balance a 30 kg child 1 metre from it.

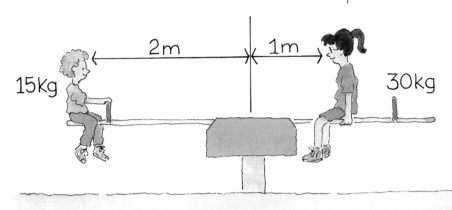

2m   1m

15kg   30kg

A light child balancing a heavy one on a seesaw

Another example of a turning force in use is opening a door. It is harder to open a door – more push is required – if it is pushed at a point closer to the hinges. To generate the same turning effect at such a short distance from the pivot, a large force has to be exerted.

Floating and sinking

Whether something floats or sinks in a liquid depends on:

◆ the material the object is made of;
◆ the liquid the object is placed in.

It may also depend on:

◆ the object's shape.

When objects are placed in water, the water pushes up on them. This upward force can be experienced by trying to push a ping-pong ball down into water. Alternatively, the effect of the upthrust can be seen by releasing the ball from below the water surface. Another good demonstration is to weigh a string bag of oranges in water and in air. The oranges weigh much less in water, because the water provides an upthrust.

A cork floats in water. When it does so, the forces on it are in balance. The downward pull on the cork (that is, its weight) equals the upwards push of the water on it. An iron ball sinks in water. The weight of the ball is greater than the upward push that the water can provide – though there is still an upward push, as is shown by the experiment with the oranges, which also sink.

Children often think that floating and sinking are determined by the weight of objects. However, it is easy to show that grains of sand, which are very light, sink. It is not the weight of the object that is important but its **density** (its mass divided by its volume) compared with the density of water. The cork floats because it is lighter than an identical amount (volume) of water. The iron ball sinks because it is heavier than an identical amount of water. An object floats if it is less dense than water, and sinks if it is more dense.

Density is a property of a material, not of a particular object. That is, iron balls can be smaller or larger, and so lighter or heavier, but the ratio of their mass to their volume is always the same.

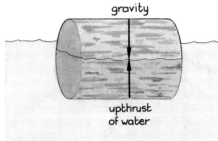

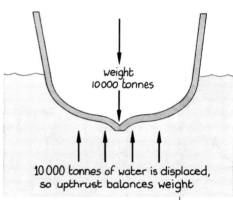

Forces acting on a floating cork

The fact that different liquids have different densities can be experienced directly. If you swim in the sea, which is slightly denser than fresh water because of the salt in it, you are more buoyant than in a fresh water swimming pool.

A material that normally sinks can be made to float by forming it into a hollow shape, so that it displaces more water than a solid body of that material would. Thus an iron ship will float. As the diagram below shows, most of the volume of the ship that is under water is occupied not by iron but by air.

A material that sinks can sometimes be made to float in another way. For example, a flat piece of metal foil will sink if dropped into water but may float if placed gently on the water surface. This is caused by something called **surface tension,** which is caused by forces attracting the molecules (particles) of water to each other. (These are not gravitational forces but electrical in nature, and no attempt will be made to explain them here.) The attraction is equal in all directions. At the surface the top layer of molecules has no water molecules above it to attract. To balance the forces here there has to be a larger sideways pull, as shown below. This extra attraction between the molecules makes it harder to push something through the surface of the water than it is to push it through the water under the surface. Surface tension is strong enough to support very light objects such as pond skaters.

Forces on an iron ship

How attraction between water molecules causes surface tension

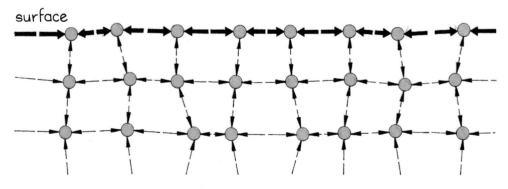

surface

Children often think that buoyancy (the extent to which something floats) varies according to the volume of water in which an object is floating. This implies that a boat will float higher in a deep lake than a shallow pond. Clearly such a view is wrong, as can be demonstrated by floating the same object in transparent tanks of different size.

Floating and sinking in air?

The same principles apply to objects in gases. An object in air pushes some of the air out of the way. The air in turns pushes back on the object and this generates an upthrust. For most objects the upthrust is insignificant. But the force can have an influence on some very light objects. Helium is a gas much lighter than air. A helium-filled balloon rises because the upthrust of the displaced air on the balloon is greater that the combined weight of helium and balloon. It continues to rise until it reaches a height where the air is thin enough for the upthrust to be balanced by gravity.

Pressure and force

These two words are often used interchangeably in everyday speech, but scientifically they are not the same thing. A force is a push or pull of a certain size. Pressure is a measure of force per unit of area over which it is applied. Imagine a woman who has a mass of 50 kg, so that she exerts a downward force of 500 newtons. She is wearing a pair of flat heeled shoes. The area of one heel is 2000 square millimetres. She stands balanced on one heel on a wooden floor. The pressure she is applying is $500 \div 2000 = 0.25$ newtons per square millimetre. Now she takes off her flat shoes and puts on a pair with stiletto heels. The area of each heel is 5 square millimetres. When she balances on one heel she is now exerting a pressure of $500 \div 5 = 100$ newtons per square millimetre, a pressure high enough to make a dent in the floor. Yet the downward force she exerts is the same. This explains why people in cold countries may wear snowshoes to walk across snow. These have a much larger area than ordinary shoes. The person's weight is spread out over that larger area and so the pressure on the snow is less than if he wore ordinary shoes. He or she is therefore less likely to sink into the snow.

The pressure of the air at sea level is 100 000 newtons per square metre. Thus if you imagine one square metre of ground, the size of the force acting is 100 000 newtons, equivalent to a 1 tonne mass resting on it.

The difference between force and energy

This bothers many people. The scientific definitions are, in ordinary language, as follows. Forces act and cause movement. The release of energy enables forces to be produced, for instance to turn a car engine or to pedal a bicycle.

Thus a force is something that happens, and can exist only while it is happening, and is applied to an object. Energy is something that can reside in an object, and can be stored in it, or released from it and transferred to another object. When I warm a block with a gas flame, I transfer energy released in the flame to the block. When I stop heating it, it retains the energy I transferred. If I push on the block, the force will make it move, but as soon as I stop pushing, the force is no longer acting and is not hidden in the block. This may seem a subtle difference but it is an important one. The subject of energy is more fully covered in the *Energy* teachers' guide.